IN PURSUIT OF ANTIQUITY

IN PURSUIT
OF ANTIQUITY

CHINESE PAINTINGS

OF THE MING AND CH'ING DYNASTIES

FROM THE COLLECTION

OF MR. AND MRS. EARL MORSE

BY

RODERICK WHITFIELD

WITH AN ADDENDUM BY WEN FONG

THE ART MUSEUM

PRINCETON UNIVERSITY

IN PURSUIT OF ANTIQUITY
is the catalogue of an exhibition of paintings
by Wang Hui and other Ming and Ch'ing masters,
held at the Art Museum of Princeton University
from May seventeenth through July twenty-seventh
nineteen hundred and sixty-nine.

The catalogue was edited and designed by
Hedy Backlin-Landman.
Typography by P. J. Conkwright.

Composition by The Anthoensen Press.
Printed by The Meriden Gravure Co.
Copyright 1969 by THE ART MUSEUM
PRINCETON UNIVERSITY
Library of Congress Card No. 70-86877

Contents

Foreword

IN the era of Professor George Rowley, initiator of the program of study of Far-Eastern Art at Princeton, scholarship in his chosen field of Chinese painting had to be, of necessity, largely speculative and conjectural. His *Principles of Chinese Painting*, published in 1947, provided significant general guidelines to scholarship and connoisseurship in a pioneering field.

In recent years more specific inquiries into the subject have been made by Rowley's successor at Princeton, Professor Wen Fong. His encouragement of Mr. and Mrs. Morse to assemble this remarkable group of works of art centering on Wang Hui and extending to related masters, and to present them to a wider public through this exhibition, attests to his increasing efforts to provide both students and public with the opportunity to consider in depth some of the major achievements of the Ming and Ch'ing painters.

The present scholarly catalogue of the Morse Collection by Dr. Roderick Whitfield now represents the work of a third generation of Princeton scholars in this field.

The generosity with which Mr. and Mrs. Morse have made their collection available for study to graduate students and assistants in the Department of Art and Archaeology during the past years demonstrates their deep interest in the furthering of scholarship in the field of Chinese painting. A collection such as theirs is an inexhaustible source for inquiry into various aspects of Chinese painting, and will be of continuing importance to teaching and research in coming years when it will have found a permanent home in the Art Museum.

This catalogue is proof of the opportunities for research offered to young scholars by a collection that is encompassing and well focussed at the same time. It is the hope of this exhibition, the first to explore an individual Far-Eastern painter and his circle, that it will not only help to re-create a major artistic personality but also to define the nature of the Orthodox movement in seventeenth-century Chinese painting.

My debt to Mr. and Mrs. Morse; to Professor Fong; to Dr. Whitfield; to Mrs. Hedy Backlin-Landman, editor of the catalogue, and to my dedicated staff in assembling the exhibition cannot be overestimated and is here acknowledged with deep appreciation.

PATRICK J. KELLEHER
Director

FRONTISPIECE: DETAIL OF "LANDSCAPE" BY CH'EN HUNG-SHOU (NO. 6)

In Pursuit of Antiquity

an exhibition of Chinese paintings
of the Ming and Ch'ing dynasties
from the collection of Mr. and Mrs. Earl Morse,
is being shown at the following museums:

The Art Museum, Princeton University,
May 17-July 27, 1969

Royal Ontario Museum, Toronto,
September 7-October 31, 1969

Nelson Gallery-Atkins Museum, Kansas City,
November 16-December 31, 1969

H. M. de Young Museum, San Francisco,
February 1-March 15, 1970

Los Angeles County Museum of Art,
April 21-May 31, 1970

Seattle Art Museum,
July 1-August 16, 1970

University of Michigan Art Museum,
September 14-October 25, 1970

Metropolitan Museum of Art, New York,
November 17-January 4, 1971

Rose Art Gallery, Brandeis University,
February 26-April 1, 1971

Elvejem Art Center, The University of Wisconsin,
April 23-June 6, 1971

Art Institute of Chicago,
June 27-July 25, 1971

British Museum, London
January-February, 1972

Preface

IT is almost fifteen years since we acquired the first of the paintings in this exhibition, the "Wisteria Blossom Studio" by the seventeenth-century master Wang Hui, painted when he was eighty years old. A short time later it was joined by another work of his, in the style of Huang Kung-wang, painted when Wang Hui was only twenty-eight years old. Many years later still, these two paintings spanning a fifty-year period were to be the start of a collection of the works of Wang Hui covering every decade of his long and productive working life.

In the last few years, under the enthusiastic and scholarly tutelage of Professor Wen Fong of Princeton University, eight other examples were assembled, filling in the highly creative accomplishments of this artist. All were acquired with the help of dealers in New York City. One more painting by Wang Hui, a fine example from his Palace Period, 1691-1698, we found, in company with Mr. C. C. Wang, in a dark corner of the saleroom at an auction. Both in time and in character, this painting adds another dimension to the collection.

Thus, by strange coincidence, the hope expressed by Soame Jenyns in the preface to the new edition of *A Background to Chinese Painting* was realized: "I should like to see a far greater number of studies of individual painters complete with a large number of illustrations showing their early and late dated works, together with contemporary copies and other imitations." More important was the fact that Professor Fong was inspired by the completeness of this artistic biography to write a scholarly treatise on Wang Hui, to be published in the near future, which further encouraged us to extend the collection to include the origins of the Orthodox School of the seventeenth century. Naturally, in that regard, one would seek a painting by Tung Ch'i-ch'ang, the founder of this seventeenth-century revival of the classic styles of the Sung and Yüan periods. Fortunately we were able to find a most satisfying example of his work.

To complete the list of the mentors of Wang Hui there recently came from Japan the painting by Wang Chien and finally that by Wang Shih-min. No master could have been more proud of his pupil nor more lavish in his praise than the latter: his adulation of Wang Hui has been generously spelled out in the colophons in this collection.

This period of Chinese art history is completed by the inclusion of a landscape painting by Yün Shou-p'ing, the close friend and contemporary of Wang Hui, who is better known for his flower paintings. The painting signed "Huang Kung-wang" in the collection was for a time also thought to be by him, but, being ever-reminiscent of the style and talent of Wang Hui, it can now be confidently attributed to the latter. Other paintings, chosen to represent the history of the Orthodox School, are by followers of Wang Hui: Yang Chin and Fang Shih-shu.

As collectors will understand, it is hard to bring a collecting project to a conclusion. Hence we could not resist subsequent opportunities to acquire examples from the earlier Ming period—by Shen Chou, T'ang Yin, and Wen Cheng-ming —as well as paintings of later Ming masters. In this latter group, we found very satisfying the highly individual talent of Ch'en Hung-shou in his dramatic paintings in the blue-green style, as well as the almost abstract painting "Red Friend" by Lan Ying, which is so easily understood and appreciated in contemporary Western terms.

Since one of the great challenges in the study and collection of Chinese painting lies in the problem of authenticity, we have included in the exhibition three imitations and a contemporary seventeenth-century replica. When a copy carries only the signature of the copied painter, in the West it is considered a forgery, intended to deceive. While forgeries seem to appear whenever there is an interest and a demand for paintings, the problem in the East is more complicated. Many copies were made as exercises in artistic virtuosity, others in adulation of the earlier masters, or as a means of recording the character and existence of important works in famous collections. We know also of examples where a master such as Tung Ch'i-ch'ang signed a creditable work of a pupil as a means of financial assistance to the latter.

The first of our copies, represented to be by the great Yüan master Huang Kung-wang, has already been mentioned; it can now be identified as the work of Wang Hui. The second, purporting to be by Wang Hui himself, is most probably a modern work. The third, the "Wu-t'ung Tree" attributed to Wang Meng, may be, in the view of current scholarly opinion, a painting by Wen Po-jen, nephew of the earlier Ming master Wen Cheng-ming. One can speculate that the skill of his copy was such that the artist placed the seal of Wang Meng on it out of pride in his own virtuosity. Finally, and of the greatest interest and importance, the large landscape of 1672 in the style of Chü-jan is an eighteenth-century exact replica of a masterpiece by Wang Hui, copied complete, including the extensive colophons by Wang Hui's teachers, Wang Shih-min and Wang Chien.

It has been an exhilarating experience to assemble the collection and to participate in the preparations for the exhibition. We are deeply grateful to Professor Patrick J. Kelleher, Director of the Art Museum of Princeton University, and his staff for making this exhibition possible, and to Mrs. Hedy Backlin-Landman in particular, who contributed her skill as the perceptive editor of this publication and made many imaginative suggestions for the exhibition itself.

The many meetings with Dr. Roderick Whitfield have enriched our own understanding of the paintings in this collection while bringing to us a gifted and delightful friend. Our thanks are due him for his skill and scholarship and for writing, while a Fellow of St. John's College, Cambridge, this most informative and interesting catalogue. We are indebted to him also for his skill in the presentation of the paintings in this exhibition for which he came especially from his new position at the British Museum.

Mr. John Hay, Dr. Whitfield's successor as the Assistant in the Far Eastern Art Seminar at Princeton University, was extremely helpful with the many details in the preparatory stages of the catalogue and the exhibition.

Our thanks go to the dealers without whose enthusiastic support our collection could not have been assembled: Miss Alice Boney of Tokyo, who started us on this fascinating road; Mr. Frank Caro of New York; Mr. Ned Owyang of the Mi Chou

Gallery, also in this city; and finally, Mrs. T. F. M. Adams of Tokyo.

No exhibition of Chinese paintings in this country could fail to include examples that have been studied and preserved by the great connoisseur and scholar, Mr. C. C. Wang. In addition to making available some of the paintings from his extraordinary collection, his appreciative counsel, helpfulness, and friendship must here be recorded.

Finally, our thanks go to Professor Wen Fong who with vision, enthusiasm, and scholarship has made this project possible. With gentle but firm hand, he has led us through the labyrinths of delights and concerns of assembling a collection of this kind. For the new vistas he has opened up to us and, more important, for his warm friendship, we will ever be grateful.

In appreciation of Professor Fong's scholarly work on the paintings by Wang Hui, Mrs. Morse and I have promised the Wang Huis in our collection to the Art Museum of Princeton University. It is our hope that the rest of our paintings will some day also go to Princeton, so that the collection may remain intact as an entity for teaching and research purposes.

EARL MORSE

New York
August, 1968

POSTSCRIPT. After Dr. Whitfield's manuscript had gone to the printer, we acquired three additional paintings: Wang Hui's "Snow Scene" and two extraordinary handscrolls by Wang Yüan-ch'i and Wu Li. We are grateful to Professor Fong for writing the scholarly addendum dealing with these paintings. E. M.

Chronological List of Painters

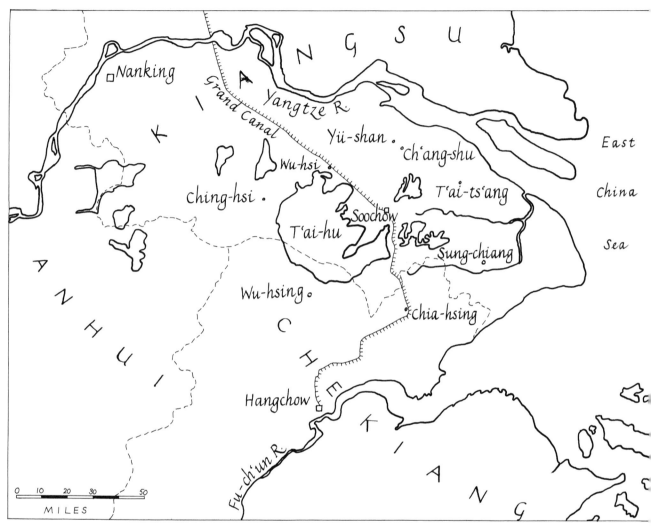

Map of the Chiang-nan Regio

Wang Hui and the Orthodox School

by Roderick Whitfield

THE Morse Collection was born in the belief that the seventeenth century was both a proper and a rewarding place to enter the study of Chinese painting. Alone among collections of Far Eastern art it was begun with a search for major works covering the whole career of a single artist, Wang Hui. In order to show him at his best and in his historical context, Mr. and Mrs. Morse added to these paintings works by Wang Hui's teachers, contemporaries and successors in the Orthodox School, as well as selected works by some of the principal masters of the Ming Dynasty highlighting the developments that led to the formation of the Orthodox School.

The collection as shown in this exhibition therefore spans a period from the late fifteenth to the early eighteenth century. Thanks to excellent advice from dealers and from Professor Fong, Mr. and Mrs. Morse have completed this collection in the short space of three or four years. Their experience cannot fail to be an encouragement to collectors in the field of Chinese painting, and an example to scholars.

It remains to me to express my warmest gratitude to Mr. and Mrs. Earl Morse for the privilege of writing this introduction and catalogue; to Professor Wen Fong of Princeton University for his continued advice and encouragement; to Dr. Richard M. Barnhart of Yale University for his draft of the catalogue entries for the Wang Hui paintings; to Mrs. Hedy Backlin-Landman of the Princeton University Art Museum for her excellent editorial assistance; to Mr. John Hay, formerly at Princeton University and now at the National Palace Museum, Taiwan, and to Mrs. Lucy Lo, his successor at the Princeton East-Asian Art Seminar, for their generous help at many stages; finally, to the Master and Fellows of St. John's College, Cambridge, for enabling me, as one of their number, to devote my time to the catalogue that follows.

R. W.

St. John's College, Cambridge
August, 1968

I

FOR an introduction to Chinese painting, one cannot do better than to choose the seventeenth century, and particularly the early years of the Ch'ing dynasty. In this period of great artistic activity, one group, without abandoning the ideas of scholar-painting, enjoyed both success and court favor. They were men who followed the precepts and example of the late Ming scholar, painter and theorist Tung Ch'i-ch'ang, in order to give painting a new purpose by creating an orthodox style. This was based on the thorough study of ancient masters and gave new life to the chief glories of earlier masterpieces.

Wang Hui, the principal figure in this exhibition, was the must successful of Tung Ch'i-ch'ang's followers, both in his mastery of the art of painting, and in the fame which he enjoyed in his own day. The paintings by Wang Hui in the Morse Collection represent every decade of his long career: both the remarkable variety of past styles that he mastered, and the development of his personal style, from the time when he was a diligent student of Wang Shih-min and Wang Chien, to his independent success, and finally to the last years of his life. They exemplify all the major problems and solutions in late seventeenth-century painting and as such have already formed the basis of a full-length monograph on the artist by Professor Wen Fong of Princeton University.[1]

The history of the line of painters leading to Wang Hui and the Orthodox School is that of *wen-jen-hua*, or scholar-painting. This had been the dominant ideal in landscape painting since the Yüan period, followed by all save the professional and court painters during a comparatively short period of brilliance in the Ming. The scholar-painters, having begun by working in the styles of the various Yüan masters, came to use them as alternative expressive modes, chosen according to the nature of the subject or the mood of the artist. From this to the "transformation" of the same styles by Tung Ch'i-ch'ang (1555-1636) and the early Ch'ing orthodox painters was but a further step. In it they sought, through diligent study of the models and through a conscious abstraction of calligraphic qualities, to obtain the same intrinsic values that they saw in the originals.

---

[1] Wen Fong, *Wang Hui (1632-1717) and his "Great Synthesis,"* forthcoming.

To guide them, the painters of the Orthodox School had Tung Ch'i-ch'ang's grand statement of the scholar-painting tradition in China. Divorcing it entirely from the work of the professional and court painters, he traced a line of direct ancestry, through Shen Chou and the Wu School in the fifteenth century, back to the Four Masters of the Late Yüan in the fourteenth, to Tung Yüan and Chü-jan in the tenth, and finally to Wang Wei, equally renowned as painter and as poet, in the eighth century.

Tung Ch'i-ch'ang's impressive pedigree has its basis in fact, as we shall presently see when we consider the stylistic origins for the work of the Yüan masters; but the ideal of scholar-painting had really emerged only in the eleventh century and had reached its height in the fourteenth. It was Su Shih who, in the eleventh century, first expressed the views of the gentleman- or scholar-painter, scorning those who judged a painting merely by its likeness to life. Instead, he preferred certain subjects—rocks, bamboo, landscape—whose reality lay deeper than their changing appearances. Even so, Su Shih does not himself seem to have attempted landscape painting, and we have to await the reunification of China under the Yüan, after the division in the time of Southern Sung, both for important developments in the theory of *wen-jen-hua* and for their acceptance in practice.

Chao Meng-fu (1254-1322)—himself a brilliant painter and calligrapher, and the first to practice what he taught—was responsible for the developments in theory: "In my painting," he wrote, "things may look simple and careless, yet a knowledgeable person will understand that they are close to ancient styles." Here is both Su Shih's fine disregard for professional finish, and a new respect for the achievements of earlier masters, which was to stay with scholar-painting during the rest of its history. Only one further element was needed to complete the criteria for scholar-painting and to ensure its later success, and this too was supplied by Chao Meng-fu: calligraphy. He suggested that the techniques required for certain styles of writing might be applied to certain subjects in painting: for example, that one should learn the formal, *pa-fen* style of writing before attempting to paint bamboo. But Chao Meng-fu's recognition of the close kinship of painting and calligraphy went beyond the merely technical: it meant that painters were now free literally to write out their paintings, and thus to bring to landscape painting that freedom from the need to be lifelike that Su Shih had admired.

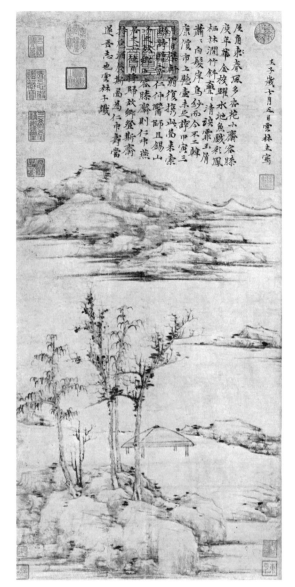

Fig. 1

Fig. 2

Those who did so were the hermit-painters of the Yüan period: hermits because under the Mongols scholars could no longer look forward to the traditional career in office for which their education prepared them. Even those born after the beginning of the Mongol rule found it hard to serve the new régime, so strong was the feeling of revolt at foreign and uncultured domination of Chinese soil. The principal painters of this time, known as the Four Masters of the Late Yüan, all lived in retirement. This is reflected in their painting—landscapes in which a single fisherman, or a group of scholars, are alone among the mountains and rivers, seeking to forget the troubles of the world. Their protest is reflected also in their common rejection of academic standards and adoption of calligraphic techniques which allowed them, in the words of Ni Tsan (1301-1374), one of the four, to "write their ideas" (*hsieh-i*). Ni Tsan's "Jung-hsi Studio" of 1372 (Fig. 1) is an example of this, both in the harmony between the artist's inscription and his painting, and in the extreme simplicity of the latter. By contrast, Wang Meng's (1308-1385) "Elegant Gathering Among Forests and Streams" of 1367 (Fig. 2) seems at first sight to be a painting of a different order, closely woven with many light touches of the brush. Yet here too is the same new-found calligraphic freedom of expression, achieved through mastery of brush and ink, without the need for the professional's attention to the correct rendering of every detail of the subject.

Huang Kung-wang (1269-1354) was the senior of the four, and with Wang Meng had the greatest following in later centuries. A handscroll, "Dwelling in the Fu-ch'un Mountains," dated 1350, is in the National Palace Museum (Fig. 3). The painting unrolls in a succession of mountains, trees and water composed of the same few elements and simple but endlessly varied brushstrokes and ink tones. Looking at it, one can appreciate the statement made by Tung Ch'i-ch'ang that Huang Kung-

Fig. 3

Fig. 5

Fig. 4

wang was the first to "lodge joy in his painting" (*chi lo yü hua*). With marvelous clarity of structure, he has been able to show a scene as varied and complex as any in Chinese landscape painting. For comparable grandeur and monumentality it must be set next to the great landscapes of the Northern Sung (Figs. 5, 7). Less daunting in scale, however, the "Fu-ch'un Mountains" almost invite the spectator to ramble in their valleys and up their slopes. Figures and houses are on a scale consistent with the trees and mountains, not dwarfed by them.

Wu Chen (1280-1354) shares the qualities of the other Yüan hermit-painters.

23

Fig. 7

Fig. 6

His "Hermit Fisherman on Lake Tung-t'ing" (Fig. 4), dated 1341, is the earliest of the examples of their work, and most clearly shows the sources of their brush styles. Tung Ch'i-ch'ang identified these sources as the tenth-century masters Tung Yüan and Chü-jan, and indeed the links are clearly to be seen in extant works: for example, the "Wintry Forests on Lake Shores" (Fig. 5) attributed to Tung Yüan, and the "Seeking the Tao in Autumn Mountains" attributed to Chü-jan (Fig. 6). Wu Chen's painting has the earthen slopes and the long "hemp-fiber" *ts'un* strokes used to depict them in both these earlier works, in strong contrast to the myriad "rain-drop" *ts'un* used to describe rock surfaces by the early eleventh-century master, Fan K'uan. Fan K'uan, in the famous "Travellers Among Streams and Mountains" (Fig. 7), painted the forbidding northern landscape, while Tung Yüan and Chü-jan, both southerners, depicted the gentler rhythms of the southern landscape, and to perfection. Mi Fu recognized in Tung Yüan's painting the essential character of the Chiang-nan region[2] and so it is no coincidence that the four Yüan masters, also natives of Chiang-nan, adopted the brush manner, as well as the landscape, of Tung Yüan and Chü-jan. In so doing they also realized both of Chao Meng-fu's ideals: the *ku-i* or "antique feeling," close to the ancient masters; and the adaptation of calligraphic brush techniques to painting. Thereby they laid the twin foundation of scholar-painting for later centuries.

At the same time—perhaps surprisingly—they set the mood for the scholar-painter in the Ming period, and the landscapes he was to paint. Though at the restoration of Chinese rule in 1368 there had been a revival of Chinese institutions so that there was no need to remain in obscurity, Shen Chou (1427-1509) and many of his followers in the Wu (Soochow prefecture) School chose to live in retirement, or rather, not to follow a career in government. Scholar-painting remained a form of escape: but the only protest left was that against academic painting, or against the rival followers of Tai Chin in the Che (Chekiang) School. The individual brush manners of the Four Masters offered inexhaustible possibilities to the scholar-painter: he was limited only by his command of brush and ink. This should not be taken to imply that the scholar-painter was unoriginal: skill in mastering the Yüan idioms may have been a major concern, but the aim was a harmony of subject, style and inscription that bespeaks a scholar's personal insight in painting.

II

Shen Chou's painting in the Morse Collection (No. 1) is a long handscroll in ink on paper. It begins with the title, "Autumn Colors Among Streams and Mountains," in four large characters, with the signature and seals of Shen Chou. Following the title, the opening section of the painting is in Ni Tsan's style, sparing of ink and form, presenting a contrast to the bold characters of the title. A diminutive figure sets out toward the familiar Ni Tsan theme of sparse trees, low shelter and a

[2] Mlle Vandier-Nicolas' translation from Mi Fu's *Hua-shih:* "C'est bien là tout le Kiang-nan" (N. Vandier-Nicolas, *Le Houa-che de Mi Fou (1051-1107)*, Paris, 1964, p. 37).

distant mountain shore. Here the theme is interpreted in a horizontal format, foreground and far distance facing each other across a long diagonal expanse of water. The composition is very similar to one of Shen Chou's most brilliant works (dated 1503)[3] in which the loneliness and distance are even more strikingly conveyed.

Between Shen Chou and Ni Tsan himself, however, there is a substantial gap, felt as keenly by Shen Chou as by ourselves when we compare the work of the two artists. In Ni Tsan's "Jung-hsi Studio" (Fig. 1) the elements are brushed in fine lines with dry ink, every stroke a delicate touch, imparting an ethereal quality to his landscape. The same forms, painted by Shen Chou (detail 1a) are done with thicker strokes, far removed from Ni Tsan's. The differences are clearly seen in the vegetation dots that seem to rush over Shen Chou's hills while in Ni Tsan's work they lie quietly on the rocks. Yet somehow Shen Chou successfully interprets the atmosphere and mood of Ni Tsan, so that we notice quickly the subtle clues that mark the transition to the fuller, rounder style of Huang Kung-wang in the next section (detail 1b).

At first there are pale wash silhouettes of distant peaks, then vertical strokes for tree trunks, some of which have a few of the horizontal foliage dots seen in the "Fuch'un Mountains" scroll by Huang Kung-wang (Fig. 3). From low-lying hills the scene changes to a line of cliffs, undercut by rapids, with the emphasis on the vertical. At the highest point are more and taller trees, well-clothed in the familiar horizontal dots, and a group of buildings half-hidden behind the slopes. Below, on the strand by the rapids, is a group of three trees with dense foliage. Further on are more low hills with trees growing thick along the ridge, then water and a boat. In a later section the scenery changes again, and with it the brush techniques. Here are great masses of rounded rock, with smaller boulders clustering closely at their bases (detail 1c). Both are modeled in soft thick strokes, curving with the rock surface and darkest at the base. Nearby are rocks of a very different kind, long, steeply shelving platforms with split faces. These are executed in long unbroken strokes made with an oblique brush. Here Shen Chou changes to the manner of Wu Chen, with more of the rounded, clustered boulders, followed by long low banks with groups of tall, thickly drawn trees, reeds and more trees.

In Shen Chou's hand at the end of the scroll is a poem, acknowledging his in-

[3] *Shina Nanga Taisei*, Tokyo 1935, vol. 16, pls. 34-35.

debtedness to Ni Tsan, though modestly disclaiming that his own painting could approach Ni Tsan's sparing methods and fullness of meaning. The calligraphy, closely modeled on that of Huang T'ing-chien (1050-1110), is strong, though not as massive as in the title; the blunt strokes accord well with the brushwork in the painting. Lastly, to complete this work of poetry, calligraphy and painting, there follows, on Shen Chou's original paper, a colophon by Yao Shou (1423-1495) with praise for a composition simple in form and structure.

For Shen Chou, poetry and letters, calligraphy and painting, were a way of life. He came from a family of scholars and painters, and felt no need to seek a career in government. T'ang Yin (1470-1523), on the other hand, was a merchant's son who secured an excellent education, but whose chances of an official career were ruined by an unfortunate incident. Intellectually brilliant, he had the chance of joining the artistic and scholarly circles of Soochow. He was at one time a pupil of Shen Chou, and Shen Chou's chief follower Wen Cheng-ming (1470-1559) was his exact contemporary and close friend. Wen Cheng-ming's father, Wen Lin, befriended him and with others encouraged his studies. In 1497 T'ang Yin gained first place in the provincial examinations and would have achieved the same distinction at the capital in the following year; but another candidate, a friend of his, had apparently gained knowledge in advance of the examination questions. Although it is not clear whether T'ang Yin was in fact also guilty, or whether the whole case was due to the jealousy of a fellow-candidate, T'ang Yin was stripped of his honors. He refused the minor post still open to him, and tried to drown his disappointment in a life of wine and pleasure. Meanwhile he had to sell his paintings to earn a living. Those that were most appreciated were of Soochow beauties (his sharp line was also admirably suited for translation into woodcut illustration), but his yearning to escape the cares of the world is evident also in his landscapes, and particularly in the album of eight leaves, now mounted as a handscroll, in the Morse collection (No. 2). His theme is presented in the poem on the first leaf (2A):

> Hsün-yang need not be the end of the world,
> On both banks the wind is fresh among the flowering rushes.
> Who is the officer Po
> Listening to the *p'i-p'a* in mid-river by the bright moon?

27

Po Chü-i's celebrated poem, the *P'i-p'a hsing*, was a long lament written in exile in 815; T'ang Yin's feeling is that only in solitude, or like Po Chü-i with a friend, can he forget cares and enjoy himself in idleness. Thus Hsün-yang (Chiu-chiang, Kiangsi province), the remote place of Po Chü-i's exile, is for T'ang Yin a place out of time and beyond care, a refuge even when the elements are inhospitable. The same chord is echoed in other leaves: "I am as carefree as the wind on the clouds"; "here indeed is a carefree solitary place"; and again in the poems by Wen Cheng-ming on two of the leaves: "the man of *tao* enjoys the flavor of his idleness"; "this is the very place where a poet finds his poems, a trace of mountain scenery falls upon the man singing in his saddle." The last metaphor seems to imply that the painter himself has become part of the remote landscape.

With T'ang Yin, the equation of poetry, calligraphy and painting has quite a different solution than with Shen Chou. Shen Chou's long handscroll is written out in a single composition, his thought and hand intent on his continuation of Ni Tsan's conception and on the various expressive possibilities of the Yüan styles. The poem at the end explains his idea, and its large clear brushstrokes accord perfectly with the blunt brushstrokes of the painting. T'ang Yin's paintings, using ink and colors on silk rather than ink on paper, seem by comparison to take a mastery of pictorial effect for granted. Their visual richness may be seen in leaf 2E, where the poem reads:

> Torrents of driving and flying rain;
> Being fearful at heart, my road becomes more difficult.
> Vaguely I make out a distant bank
> And rejoice that it is Huang's home.

These lines are given vivid interpretation in the darkened, rain-torn sky and the tormented branches of the foreground trees, as well as in the figures who struggle to reach the shelter of a friend's house.

A distinctive characteristic of T'ang Yin's style is the *tsa-pi* or "rubbed-brush" technique used for the modeling of the rocks. The brush was held at a slant, so that the stroke has one even and sharp edge, made by the point of the brush. The sharp edges and the use of graded ink washes give a brilliant appearance not unlike the landscapes of the Che School painters. T'ang Yin, in fact, though he was a Wu painter, was close to the professionals, both because he depended on painting for a living and because of the ink-wash idiom he used. Between him and Shen Chou we may make the distinction (first stated by Kuo Hsi in the twelfth century) that exists between the *shih-shan* or rocky mountain (cf. Fan K'uan, Fig. 7), and the *t'u-shan* or earthen mountain (cf. Tung Yuan, Fig. 5). We have seen in Shen Chou that a blunt brushstroke, carefully hiding the point of the brush, was the essential element in painting the soft rounded contours of the earthen mountain. T'ang Yin by contrast rejoices in the slanted brush and in the pictorial contrasts to be obtained from the various ink tones and the tone of the silk where it is left blank. Shen Chou's was the scholar's calligraphic alternative, T'ang Yin's the professional painter's; yet T'ang Yin's brilliance in letters, and his escapist philosophy, assured his acceptance and appreciation by the scholar-painters.

III

T'ang Yin, Shen Chou and many of the latter's followers were natives of Soochow, which was a center for scholars and literary men and China's most cultured city in the fifteen and sixteenth centuries. Set in Chiang-nan, one of China's best rice-, tea- and fruit-growing areas, Soochow is not far south of the Yangtze, with the T'ai Lake to the west and Hangchow to the south. Its position on the Grand Canal, which supplied the capital whether in the south or in the north, assured Soochow's prosperity. During the Southern Sung the finest silks for the court at Hangchow were of Soochow manufacture. The city's site and surroundings might easily compete with Hangchow's in beauty. Hangchow has the famous West Lake; Soochow, circled by a canal, is intersected within the walls by many more, so that the pattern of canals and bridges is a distinctive feature of the city. Poets since T'ang and Sung times have praised the beauties of the region; the Four Masters of the Late Yüan were born there, and it was the landscape of their paintings. Many of the famous beauty spots in the country around Soochow and the neighboring great lake, T'ai-hu, were accessible by water and provided ideal venues for the elegant parties of Soochow's literary circles.

The album by Wen Cheng-ming in the Morse collection (No. 3) is intimately connected with the Soochow that he and his friends knew and loved. Whereas T'ang Yin's album reflects his many excursions into the surrounding region, Wen

Cheng-ming brings us to Soochow itself, to the many gardens within the walls. Though the garden in question is not named in this album, it is evidently the same as that which Wen Cheng-ming had illustrated in a similar but larger album in 1535, the Cho-cheng-yüan (Garden of the Unsuccessful Politician). A garden of the same name still exists in Soochow. The Cho-cheng-yüan was established on the site of a temple by the Censor Wang Hsien-ch'en in the Chia-ching reign (1522-1567). Wen Cheng-ming's album of 1535 has thirty-one leaves and amounts to a very full description of the garden, each leaf depicting a particular corner, pavilion or piece of water, accompanied by a poem and a prose note indicating its position in the garden. In a fairly long inscription at the end, Wen Cheng-ming describes the garden as a whole, and its history. The Morse album does not have such an inscription, nor does it mention the name of the owner of the garden; its eight leaves represent a selection from the larger album, having the same poems as the latter, but paintings composed entirely anew. On the last page, in place of the usual prose note on the subject, is the name of a studio in the garden, and Wen Cheng-ming's signature with the date 1551. Possibly, in the space of fifteen years or so, the garden, still young when he had first painted it, had changed, so that fresh viewpoints showed off its various parts to better advantage, while the same poems were still applicable. Indeed, there is a hint of this in an added note to the poem on leaf 3DD. In the 1535 album there is a prose note that "the banana enclosure is to the left of the Huai-yü-t'ing." The Morse album adds that "later, palms were planted, to make a suitable shade for the summer months." These are shown in the accompanying painting, with many other changes of the original composition of rock, banana tree and angled fence. The new elements give an added richness to the painting, while the composition and brushwork are still restrained and elegant.

Looking through the eight leaves and reading the poems opposite, one has the impression that the garden itself shared this quality of elegant restraint in its layout and planning. The first leaf (3A) gives the complete view of an open pavilion and its surrounding garden and lake. Groups of trees and a screen of bamboo form the main elements visible in the painting; the note to the poem is more eloquent on the various kinds of fragrant flowers planted there. But it seems clear that the gardens of Soochow owed their chief beauty to the harmonious combination of bamboo, trees and water. The name of Wen Cheng-ming's own garden, Yü-ch'ing shan-fang (Jade Chime Hill Cottage) gives little clue to its character, but Shen Chou's place was called Yu-chu-chü, the Dwelling with Bamboo, and T'ang Yin's, T'ao-hua-wu, Peach Blossom Bank. They were places, like the Garden of the Unsuccessful Politician, in which to forget alike the cares of the world and the heat of the noonday sun, as the poem and painting on the third leaf (3CC) of the album describe it:

> Bamboos are planted around the low mound
> Forming a bank of bamboo around the edge.
> In full summer it already seems to be autumn,
> So deep is the wood, one cannot tell when it is noon.
> In its midst is one who has abandoned the world,
> Enjoying himself with a *ch'in* and a goblet.
> When a wind stirs he too wakes from drunkeness
> To sit and listen to the rain on the bamboo leaves.

The poems are all written in a cursive script, fast but carefully controlled at every turn, with extremely fine ligatures between many of the characters. This script is close in style to a manuscript of Wen Cheng-ming's poems written out when he was in his eighty-ninth year (in 1558),[4] and to other writings in his eighties. The poems are set out less formally than in the 1535 album, without ruled squares and in a single style instead of a variety ranging from "seal" to "grass" characters.

The brushwork of the paintings, especially in the foliage patterns of bamboo, apple, etc., recalls the small *k'ai-shu* or regular script of Wen Cheng-ming's *Ch'ientzu-wen* (Thousand Character Essay) texts. The figures, scholars and their attendants, are more finely drawn than Shen Chou's: it is evident that Wen Cheng-ming was a practiced figure painter. Indeed, not only the style of his figures but their very attitudes were occasionally copied by men such as Ch'ien Ku (1508-1572) who continued in the style of Shen Chou and Wen Cheng-ming.

The antiquarianism of the scholars in the generation following Wen Chengming is epitomized by Ch'ien Ku's painting in the Morse collection (No. 4). Its subject is that most famous of all literary gatherings in China, held on a spring day

4 Reproduced in *Shōseki Meihin Sōkan*, vol. 113, Tokyo 1965.

in A.D. 353 at the Lan-t'ing or Orchid Pavilion, and recorded by Wang Hsi-chih in what has ever since been held to be the finest piece of *hsing-shu*, running script, in the history of Chinese calligraphy, the *Lan-t'ing hsü*. Recently the discovery of the engraved funerary tablet of a cousin of Wang Hsi-chih sparked a long discussion of the *Lan-t'ing hsü*, in which the authenticity even of parts of the text has been questioned. Needless to say, these considerations do not affect the whole tradition of the *Lan-t'ing-hsü*, though in this case Ch'ien Ku shows in his final inscription that he was well aware that even the best of surviving versions was not without its faults. His painting was composed at the request of a friend, with whom he had examined one of the engraved versions of the *Lan-t'ing hsü*, and at whose further request he also transcribed the texts of Wang Hsi-chih's preface and of the poems written at the gathering in 353.

The handscroll, in colors on paper, has a gay appearance. Near the beginning a figure, Wang Hsi-chih himself, surveys the scene from a pavilion. Thence winds a serpentine rill, down which attendants float a succession of cups of wine on lotus leaves. On either bank are seated the scholars, gazing for inspiration at the water, the sky, or the blank paper before them, or listening to the recitations of those who have already completed a poem. From the text we learn the statistics of the party, and the forfeits: eleven men composed two poems each, fifteen completed one; and sixteen, failing in the completion of even one poem, each drank three cups of wine.

To match the antiquarianism of the subject, the title written by Wang Ku-hsiang (1501-1568), another member of the circle of men of letters continuing the Wu tradition, is in large seal characters. Ch'ien Ku's own indebtedness to Wen Cheng-ming and mastery of his style is apparent throughout the scroll, in brush technique and in foliage patterns, but especially in the figures: comparison with the Wen Cheng-ming album examined above reveals one figure that is so close as to appear a copy.

Lan Ying (1585-1664), a native of Ch'ien-t'ang (Hangchow) in Chekiang, is traditionally held to be the last of the Che School painters in the line founded by Tai Chin (1388-1462). His place of birth and the fact that he was a professional painter have probably earned him this name. Should we judge by his painting, however, it will be hard to find traits in his style that would link him with the earlier Che masters, who painted in the ink-wash idiom of the Southern Sung period. Rather, it becomes clear that by this time the identity of the Che style had been completely submerged by the success of the Wu scholar-painters. Lan Ying's landscape paintings no longer followed the Southern Sung styles: instead, most are after the same Sung and Yüan masters, particularly Huang Kung-wang, that were studied by the Wu artists.

The painting by Lan Ying in this exhibition (No. 5), though not a landscape, well illustrates this scholarly influence in his art, and especially the calligraphic use of the brush. The title, "Red Friend," is a pun, since "red friend," besides referring to the rock in the painting, can also mean wine. The subject is a scholarly one, one of those strangely shaped rocks that we have already seen on a leaf of Wen Cheng-ming's album. The alliance of color and ink, and the stylization and abstraction of the form, are typical of the turn painting was taking in the seventeenth century.

One of the leading spirits in painting in this period of the decline of the Ming dynasty and the conquest of China by the Manchus was Ch'en Hung-shou (1598-1652). Lan Ying, meeting him as a talented boy in his tenth year, is said to have been so impressed that he gave up painting from life (*hsieh-sheng*), considering Ch'en to be his superior. Ch'en Hung-shou must have been both resourceful and independent in character: his father died when the boy was in his ninth year, and about the time that he met Lan Ying he set himself the task of mastering, from a rubbing, Li Kung-lin's figure style, and then of transforming it until his copies were no longer recognizable as such. It seems certain that his study of the figure styles of Li Kung-lin (1049-1106) and other early artists through rubbings, the most reliable and accessible medium, had a profound influence on the nature of his own style. The crisp clarity of his line may be seen in all his works, though perhaps especially in his figure paintings. Several series of woodblock book illustrations were carved from his designs; they possess a strength and a nobility unparalleled in that field.

Though Ch'en Hung-shou is known primarily for his figure painting, we have the evidence of a contemporary, Chou Liang-kung (1612-1672), who met him in 1624 and remained a lifelong friend, that Ch'en's talents went further than this: "People only know his excellence at figures, and do not know his marvelous [ability] in landscapes; people only exclaim at his strange distortions, and do not know that his every brushstroke has its foundation." The two paintings shown here (Frontispiece, Nos. 6, 7) must date to the same period in his career: the landscape is dated 1633, while the still life is undated. The latter, with its lotus flowers, its vase painted with a phoenix, and its pomegranates, lotus seed pods, roots, *ling-chih* or immortals' mushroom, and rocks all gathered in a lacquer lotus dish, would appear to have Taoist connotations; the meaning of the cloth tied around the vase is not clear. The modeling of the rocks in both paintings, in ink overlaid with color wash, is very similar. In both can be seen Ch'en's line, as sharp as the lines of a cracked pane of glass. The landscape, with its brilliant turquoise and emerald, is in full accord with *ku-i* (the antique feeling), taking the blue-and-green style of the T'ang and producing a thoroughly new interpretation of it. Superbly drawn rocks and trees, with bands of mist left in plain silk to heighten the artificial pattern of blocks of color, are here combined with two figures, both of which must count among Ch'en Hung-shou's best. The lean and elegant scholar (detail, 6a) is the very counterpart of the woodcuts after Ch'en's designs for the novels *Shui-hu chuan* and *Hsi-hsiang chi*, save that the figure illustrations of the latter are executed in more flowing lines with uninterrupted curves; those of the *Shui-hu chuan* appear closest in stance and in structure to the scholar and his attendant in the Morse landscape. Again, in the illustrations for the *Hsi-hsiang chi*, dated 1639, six years after this painting, one can see close resemblances in the rocks and trees and in the lotus flowers to those of the Morse still life.

I V

The direction taken by painters in the latter half of the sixteenth century may be gauged by Ch'ien Ku's *Lan-t'ing* handscroll (No. 4), dated 1560 and described above. Apart from the very subject—the famous gathering of scholars at the Orchid Pavilion in 353—other aspects of late Ming antiquarian interest, which encompass rubbings, seal-carving and embroidery, are seen at their best. The occasion for this painting was Ch'ien Ku's examination of a rubbing of Wang Hsi-chih's renowned piece of writing recording the event. The title by Wang Ku-hsiang, a close friend, is in seal characters, and the painter's own interest in seal carving is evident throughout the scroll, where between painting and colophons Ch'ien Ku has impressed no less than 15 of his personal seals, some of them up to five times. Brilliant in execution and completed by a thorough transcription of the *Lan-t'ing-hsü* and all the associated poems, the painting is a fine example of the late Wu School.

Outside the scholar-painting tradition, Ch'en Hung-shou's paintings (Nos, 6, 7) are examples of how much was achieved by the bold experiments of the late Ming individualists and eccentrics.[5] Many artists, however, failed to attain these standards, and in the hands of the less talented of them the traditions both of scholar-painting and of the professionals suffered a decline, and their styles and subjects became exhausted conventions. The Morse collection includes an example of this decline in a painting (No. 8) bearing the seal of the Yüan artist Wang Meng but having only a superficial resemblance to his style. Decorative but static and lifeless, it may be by a descendant of Wen Cheng-ming, possibly his nephew Wen Po-jen (1502-1575). The painting is indicative of the general state of late Ming painting, which was to cause Mo Shih-lung (d. 1587) and his younger friend, Tung Ch'i-ch'ang, so much concern.[6] For them, contemporary painters had lost not only the spirit of the ancient masters, but their paintings lacked even the basic requirements of compositional logic. Mo Shih-lung complained: "Nowadays people build up small bits to make a large mountain; this is one of the worst mistakes," his own idea being that one should first establish the larger divisions of a composition, before coming to details. We can see the justification for his complaint in the painting manuals that led eventually to the famous *Mustard Seed Garden Painting Manual* (1679), teaching painting from the basis of individual elements, presented singly and then in combination, so building a composition in precisely the manner he deplored.

The new orthodoxy that Mo Shih-lung and Tung Ch'i-ch'ang sought to set up was still based on calligraphy and on the paintings of ancient masters, but theirs was a tradition informed by study and discipline, and no blind following of previously accepted styles. Ironically, at this time when, in point of style, the chief distinctions between the painting of the scholars and that of the court and professional painters had been lost, the new orthodoxy revived the old rivalry of the Wu and Che Schools and made of it a strict demarcation between the amateur and the professional. This was done, however, not in the spirit of a revival of hostilities by the

---

[5] Many more were shown in the exhibition, *Fantastics and Eccentrics in Chinese Painting,* selected by James Cahill, Asia House Gallery, New York 1967.

[6] For a stimulating discussion of Tung Ch'i-ch'ang and his times see Nelson Wu, "Tung Ch'i-ch'ang 1555-1636: Apathy in Government and Fervor in Art," *Confucian Personalities,* edited by Arthur F. Wright and Denis C. Twitchett, Stanford University Press 1962, pp. 260-293.

scholars against an already defeated Che School, but in an attempt to define and distinguish the best approaches and solutions to the art of landscape painting.

By analogy with the two schools of Ch'an Buddhism in the T'ang dynasty, the two traditions of amateur and professional were called Southern and Northern respectively. In the Buddhist context, the Southern branch believed in enlightenment achieved suddenly, as opposed to its gradual attainment in the Northern branch. Thus in painting the term Southern was applied to the scholar-amateurs who scorned the attention to realism and detail of the professional or Northern painters.

Mo Shih-lung died in 1587, aged about 50. If it was he who initially diagnosed the malaise of contemporary painting and first sketched the division of the history of Chinese painting into two separate traditions, it was his younger contemporary, Tung Ch'i-ch'ang, who further developed his theories and provided the technical framework on which the new orthodox style could be built. For it was a paradox of the orthodox style that while the amateur ideal was held to be a perfection beyond learning, this ideal in fact required study and attention to technique on an unprecedented scale. The analogy with the Southern branch of Ch'an Buddhism was carried as far as direct descriptions of the amateur ideal in Buddhist terms: "The painter who imitates ancient masters may already be regarded as belonging to the Upper Vehicle. If he advances one more step, he adopts Nature as his teacher"; "[The Southern School master] enters the land of Tathagata Buddha in a single stroke." In other words, enlightenment is reached through intuition rather than mere attention to technical means. In the meantime, however, Tung Ch'i-ch'ang's writings abound in technical instructions, often using the example of calligraphy to make the meaning clear: "When a scholar turns to painting, he applies to it the techniques of 'grass,' 'clerical' and other exotic manners of calligraphy"; "As in writing a character, one concentrates one's power on the turning strokes. One must guard especially against letting a stroke go in one direction without checking it."

In fact, both *lin-ku* (following the ancients) and the categorization of brush patterns in more or less calligraphic terms were phenomena already well established in the Ming as the standard approach to scholar-painting. To these, Tung Ch'i-ch'ang added a most close and strict attention to compositional principles to be observed in painting. We have already noted Mo Shih-lung's complaint about contemporary painting, that instead of first planning the larger divisions of a composition, "nowadays people build up small bits to make a large mountain." Tung Ch'i-ch'ang wrote: "Outline first the general shapes and attitudes of the mountains; within the outlines, use straight modelling strokes. This is Huang Kung-wang's method." He also required a dynamic balance of parts, known as *shih* (force or momentum) and achieved through pairs of complementary principles: "If a painter can both open (*fen*) and close (*ho*) a composition, and if his modelling method is able to carry out all that he intends, then his painting will easily look convincing. ... Next, he must follow [the principle of] void and solid (*hsü-shih*). By void and solid are meant the varying degrees of complexity and brevity in brushwork in different parts of a painting. A complex area must be followed by a brief interval; the void and the solid complement one another. If the painting is too sparse, the scenery will not appear deep and distant; if it is too dense, it will lose atmosphere and resonance. Only when a painter subtly weighs the void against the solid, and presents both aspects with feeling, will his painting naturally appear exciting." Again, "when distant mountain ranges alternately rise and fall, there is force or momentum (*shih*); when sparse forest appear now high and now low, there is feeling (*ch'ing*)."

Brush techniques and compositional principles were not the whole story: all had further to depend on the painting of the ancients, particularly those who, in the Orthodox view, had laid the foundations of the Southern School. An artist was not free to invent his own style: certain brush techniques were held to be suited to particular styles or types of composition, and certain elements to have been perfected by particular artists, so that forms had been created which the orthodox artist could not abandon with impunity. Tung Ch'i-ch'ang argued: "Some say: 'One should establish one's own style.' This cannot be so. For example, for willow trees [one follows] Chao Po-chü [twelfth century]; for pine trees, Ma Ho-chih [twelfth century]; for dead branches, Li Ch'eng [919-967]. A thousand years cannot change this. Even if a painter should make variations of these types, he cannot depart from these sources. How can anyone put aside the ancient methods and start [anew] on his own?"

This being so, how was the orthodox painter to achieve originality? The answer lies in the spirit in which he approached his chosen models, and the goal is best seen in Tung Ch'i-ch'ang's own evaluations of the work of some of them. On two compositions in which Huang Kung-wang followed earlier paintings by Tung Yüan,

Tung Ch'i-ch'ang quoted a proverb: "Ice is colder than water"; of Wu Chen in a similar relation to Chü-jan, he said: "Having examined this painting, I realize that in following the master, Wu Chen has 'surpassed the indigo.'" In each case, his meaning was that the later artist had achieved something greater than his model, just as ice is colder than the water of which it is composed, and as the dye prepared from the indigo plant is more intense in color than the plant itself.

Mo Shih-lung, in a passage on the problem of imitating ancient masters, used a new term, *pien* or "metamorphosis," to describe the orthodox goal: "I once remarked that the calligraphy styles of Wang Hsi-chih [307-365] and his son were exhausted by the times of the Ch'i and the Liang [479-556]. Ever since the early T'ang, however, when Yü Shih-nan [558-638], Ch'u Sui-liang [596-658] and others brought forth a new metamorphosis of their methods, a new correspondence [to old principles] was discovered and Wang Hsi-chih and his son were suddenly alive again. At first this statement appears difficult to understand. The truth is, while copying and tracing are easy, transmission of the 'spirit and breath' (*shen-ch'i*) is most difficult. Chü-jan, Mi Fu [1051-1107], Huang Kung-wang and Ni Tsan all followed Tung Yüan ... yet each of them produced something different from the others. [But] when a common painter copies, he does something identical to his model. How can he in this way expect to influence the world?"

Significantly, Mo Shih-lung's illustrations of *pien* in the history of art are taken, the one from calligraphy, the other from examples in the continuation of Tung Yüan's style by Sung and Yüan painters. Calligraphy, then, was at the very core of the orthodox ideal, even to the point of serving as an example for the transformation of earlier styles. At the same time, Tung Yüan, some of whose paintings still survived, held a position of great importance at the head of the Southern tradition. Tung Ch'i-ch'ang's large painting in the Morse Collection, "Shaded Dwelling among Streams and Mountains" (No. 9), was made according to the inscription after a sketch taken from a painting by Tung Yüan. Though Tung Yüan's original no longer survives, it is still possible to compare Tung Ch'i-ch'ang's painting with the "Wintry Forests on Lake Shores" attributed to Tung Yüan and already used above as an example of his style.

Tung Yüan's painting (Fig. 5) is a composition in "flat distance" (*p'ing-yüan*) looking across foreground hills and trees to hills and wooded shores progressively further away. The forms are soft and gently contoured, yet clearly defined by means of light and dark modeling strokes of the kind later to be known as *p'i-ma* or hemp-fiber *ts'un*. These strokes are always subordinate to the forms they depict: hence a classical clarity reigns throughout the composition.

Tung Ch'i-ch'ang's "Shaded Dwelling among Streams and Mountains" (No. 9), by contrast, is a "high distance" (*kao-yüan*) composition, bold and massive in appearance, monumental in effect, and clearly structured. Large trees growing on a series of high banks in the foreground open the composition, which culminates in a mountain peak composed of semi-abstract rock forms juxtaposed in broad planes. Both trees and rocks are depicted in large, calligraphic brushstrokes, the effect of which is to focus attention on the structure and away from surface detail. Pockets of mist are used to articulate the composition and give it volume, just as expanses of water divide Tung Yüan's "Wintry Forests on Lake Shores." Evidently in his painting Tung Ch'i-ch'ang sought to create a composition on the majestic scale of the Northern Sung, obeying laws derived from the study of surviving masterpieces and giving the landscape details new life through the powerful abstraction of his brushwork. By any standards, he must be held to have succeeded; but it was his theories, rather than his paintings, that were to have the greatest influence on the course of Chinese painting. The paintings that follow will show how successful were his disciples, and particularly Wang Hui, in the creation of a *ta-ch'eng* or Great Synthesis of all that they held to be best in past styles.

V

Wang Hui was born in 1632 in Ch'ang-shu, Kiangsu, which was also the native town of the Yüan master Huang Kung-wang. His talents for painting developed early, if at first along conventional lines, but in 1651 he was "discovered" by the painter Wang Chien (1598-1677) who was so struck by the young man's ability that he took him into his own household to study calligraphy and, later, painting. In the following year he introduced him to the leading scholar-painter of the day, Wang Shih-min (1592-1680). This introduction, and the invitation it produced for the young painter to come and live at Wang Shih-min's studio in T'ai-ts'ang, was to be of the utmost importance for Wang Hui. Not only did he have the opportunity to study Wang Shih-min's own collection of paintings at T'ai-ts'ang and many other collections over a wide area, but Wang Shih-min became his guide also to the theories of Tung Ch'i-ch'ang, and his mentor for many years.

Wang Shih-min, the senior of the "Four Wangs" (Wang Chien and Wang Hui were the second and third, Wang Shih-min's grandson Wang Yüan-ch'i, 1642-1715, the fourth), had studied with Tung Ch'i-ch'ang and was the first to follow his precepts seriously. Wang Shih-min's painting in the Morse Collection (No. 10) is already well known through its publication in Sherman Lee's *A History of Far Eastern Art*[7] when it was in the collection of Mr. C. C. Wang. It is a landscape hanging scroll in the style of Huang Kung-wang, dated 1666. The composition is tightly knit, especially when compared with the free and open texture of Huang Kung-wang's own "Dwelling in the Fu-ch'un Mountains" (Fig. 3). Wang Shih-min has in fact analyzed Huang Kung-wang's manner in a series of motifs—mountain slopes, flat-topped peaks, rocks and trees—and described them by serried ranks of calligraphic dots and strokes. The same dots and strokes may represent trees or rocks, or merge from one to the other without a clear distinction, as do the horizontal strokes that serve equally for tree foliage and for the modeling of successive mountain folds (detail 10a). Tall columns of these horizontal strokes, laid over lighter, long *p'i-ma* or hemp-fiber strokes, are virtually the sole constituents of the boulders on the ridge leading to the summit; in the valley they are combined with vertical strokes to indicate forests. Wang Shih-min's paramount concern is in the brush pattern and movement, in the variation between light and dark tones of ink, rather than in the description of detail. Huang Kung-wang's infinitely variable dots and strokes, on the other hand, were concerned primarily with the representation of the landscape and its features. The result is that Wang Shih-min's painting is a scintillating transformation of Huang Kung-wang's style into abstract calligraphic terms.

Another seventeenth-century interpretation of Huang Kung-wang's style can be seen in Wang Chien's landscape of 1657 (No. 11). The composition, modeled on a lost painting by Huang Kung-wang that Wang Shih-min had also followed, is of a valley, closed at its far end by a sheer and massive peak. To the right, successive slopes and cliffs rise and fall in an undulating rhythm leading to this peak; opposite, trees and boulders rise in unbroken succession from the foreground to frame it on the left. The brushwork, softer than Wang Shih-min's, alternates between

[7] New York 1964, p. 441, fig. 586.

40

densely and sparsely modeled areas to heighten the effect of movement in the painting (detail 11a). Wang Chien's pupil Wang Hui follows a valley composition similar to this in a large landscape also in the style of Huang Kung-wang, dated 1660 (No. 12). In it, however, Wang Hui copies neither Huang Kung-wang nor Wang Chien, but grapples, perhaps for the first time, with the problem of organizing a large landscape design. This is his earliest dated work,[8] though an undated small album survives in the Palace Museum of Taiwan to show the early skill and inventiveness of the young painter. The present landscape of 1660 is in marked contrast to the virtuosity displayed in the album; it is as if Wang Hui had forced himself to pass over the attractions of the smaller details in order to emphasize the structure of the landscape. This is executed in clearly defined overlapping folds, plainly modeled, that carry the eye upward to the summit of the mountain (detail 12a). This powerful movement, known to Chinese critics as the *lung-mo* or dragon-vein, is an outstanding feature of Wang Hui's mature works, growing naturally out of the *shih* or momentum of the earlier orthodox painters. The dragon-vein is seen again, in a more developed form, in Wang Hui's painting of 1664 (No. 13) after the tenth-century painter Chü-jan. Professor Wen Fong has described how in this painting the individual brushstrokes serve to create the rhythms that eventually take in the whole composition: "Individual brushstrokes are now the sole conveyor of life and energy; they grow and expand continuously until the whole becomes a great flowing pattern of undulating eddies and counter-eddies, serving to 'move' peaks and valleys around. . . . The new compositional unity depends not so much on the balance and harmony of the parts, as on the kinetic energy and tension created by the individual strokes within the total structure."[9] Altogether, the painting of 1664 makes a fitting start to Wang Hui's paintings of the first decade or so of the brilliant K'ang-hsi reign (1662-1722). One can readily understand the enthusiasm of Wang Shih-min and Wang Chien for the work of their pupil, an enthusiasm abundantly expressed in their colophons to the paintings that follow.

[8] The painting listed by Sirén (*Chinese Painting*, vol. VII, p. 425) with the date of 1654 is in fact dated 1714, an error due to a misinterpretation of the cyclical date.

[9] Wen Fong, "The Orthodox Master," *Art News Annual* XXXIII, 1967.

VI

From the mid-1660s for about a decade, Wang Hui, while already a past master of his brush and ink, was still passionately engaged in searching out the secrets of the classical masters. During this time he produced the finest works of his career. A prime example is the handscroll, "The Colors of the T'ai-hang Mountains," dated 1669 (No. 14). After the title, written in archaic characters by Wang Shih-min, and Wang Hui's own inscription, we are plunged into a rocky landscape of compelling richness and grandeur. This represents his study of the heroic northern landscape of the Northern Sung, preserved for us in Fan K'uan's famous "Travellers among Streams and Mountains" (Fig. 7).

The "T'ai-hang Mountains" handscroll is also a clear illustration of Wang Hui's application of design principles both in the composition as a whole and within the various elements. Just as his individual brushstrokes, however small, have a calligraphic quality and balance, so do the elements of his composition have a movement and rhythm of their own, imparting dynamic movement to the whole composition (details 14a, b). Whereas the works of the Northern Sung are seen frontally and appear as direct statements of the grandeur of the natural world, Wang Hui's compositions, such as this handscroll, bear off the spectator with an impetus that proceeds from within the painting. Here indeed the dragon-vein is visible and vigorous, pervading every part of the composition.

Wang Shih-min was fond of saying that his pupil surpassed himself with each new painting: one might imagine that Wang Hui in "The Colors of the T'ai-hang Mountains" had reached his peak, but in the next, of 1672, there is ample justification for Wang Shih-min's praise. In Professor Fong's judgment, this painting is an exact copy of a very important missing original, which records a critical stylistic discovery by Wang Hui.[10] It is a very large hanging scroll (No. 15) after a painting by the tenth-century master, Chü-jan. The title, *Yen-fou yüan-hsiu t'u*, originally written by Emperor Hui-tsung (r. 1101-1126), was transcribed by Wang Hui in one inscription; then in a second he gave his reasons for considering Chü-jan's painting to be important: "This painting by Chü-jan does not make use of paths, streams, buildings, roads or bridges. It depends only on broad and heroic *shih* (compositional forces)."

[10] Wen Fong, "The Orthodox Master," *Art News Annual* XXXIII, 1967; and personal communication.

Here is the essence of Wang Hui's paintings. When, in the year following, he composed an album of paintings in various styles for Wang Shih-min, it was this style of Chü-jan, almost this very composition on a more modest scale, that he put at its head. Here, for Wang Hui and for the two older Wangs who added their own testimonies to the 1672 painting, was the orthodox style stripped of all non-essentials, leaving only the mountains, trees and water. Not that the exclusion of all trace of human activity, "deep in the mountains where even shepherds and wood-cutters do not reach" meant that this was a painting of actual scenery; on the contrary, this is where we should recall Tung Ch'i-ch'ang's maxim: "If one considers the uniqueness of scenery, then a painting is not the equal of real landscape. But if one considers the wonderful excellence of brush and ink, then real landscape can never equal painting."

The great mountain is described with long hemp-fiber strokes and clothed with moss-dots and dense trees deep in the valleys (detail 15a). So few are the individual motifs of the composition; yet Wang Hui used them to create the archetype of the Southern-School landscape with such effect that Wang Chien and Wang Shih-min felt no need to see the original painting by Chü-jan. In his inscription, Wang Shih-min wrote that "this painting has opened for Master Chü another existence." Wang Chien went further: "I have actually seen a living incarnation of Chü-jan."

With this transformation of Chü-jan's style in 1672, Wang Hui may be said to have achieved his aim of *ta-ch'eng* or great synthesis. He could now, in his own words, "use the brush and ink of the Yüan masters to move the peaks and valleys of the Sung." The richness of the spectrum encompassed by this formula may be seen in the album that he painted in 1673 and presented to Wang Shih-min, who inscribed it with the title: *Ch'ü-ku*, "In Pursuit of Antiquity" (No. 16a).

The first leaf (16a) is after Chü-jan, a greatly reduced version of the 1672 painting; there follow eleven leaves after painters ranging from Tung Yüan to the Yüan masters, including some more descriptive or colorful styles such as those of Kuo Hsi and Wang Shen. Liu Yü, a contemporary of Wang Hui, was obviously taken aback by the inclusion of the seventh leaf in the blue-green style of Wang Shen, "excelling in workmanship and prettiness." "Wang Shih-min," he wrote in a colophon, "collects the complete achievements (*ta-ch'eng*) of painting. His opinions must be out of the ordinary"—if he includes such works in the heritage of the Southern School. Liu Yü's attitude, however, and his preference for Wang Hui's works "in the manners of Ni Tsan, Huang Kung-wang and Ts'ao Chih-po" was outdated. As a full-time painter, Wang Hui could draw upon the best of all past styles; workmanship was implicit in his orthodox goal of transforming them through careful study and disciplined, calligraphic use of the brush. Nor was "prettiness" any longer to be despised: Wang Hui showed that a painting could be colorful and attractive without sacrificing scholarly ideals.

Wang Hui had an able defender in his lifelong friend and admirer Yün Shou-p'ing (1633-1690), who wrote many colophons in this album. Of the eighth leaf, the colorful one that had distressed Liu Yü, he wrote that he valued it more than the works of the Northern Sung painter Wang Shen himself. Yün Shou-p'ing was always keenly conscious of a painting's historical context. His colophons in the present album by Wang Hui are for the most part written on the mount next to the paintings themselves, as though to emphasize their relevance to them. Scarcely one fails to make reference to some virtue of the ancients that Yün Shou-p'ing finds brought to new life in the works of Wang Hui. In this manner his is a very real contribution to the original purpose of the album: he brings us close both to the actual creation of the paintings, and to the historical intention of Wang Hui as one who "pursued the ancients." Yün Shou-p'ing is also our chief seventeenth-century witness to Wang Hui's success: on the last leaf of the album he writes the high praise that here Wang Hui has been truly able to attain the "unconscious achievements" of the ancient masters. It is a fitting note on which to close this important work.

One further painting in the Morse Collection may rank equally with those described above as one of Wang Hui's masterpieces. It is a small hanging scroll (No. 17), dated 1675, with an inscription by Wang Chien. It is a variation, in the style of Wu Chen, of the formula used in the 1672 painting after Chü-jan, of near-abstract landscape forms in three-dimensional space. Once more it is the dragon-vein which compels attention: the whole composition seems caught up in the rhythms of the blunt hemp-fiber strokes and in the patterns of moss dots laid over them. All the parts —the trees in the right foreground, even the half-hidden group of buildings at the left—are swept up towards the center and into the involved, spiraling forms of the mountain. Small as it is, this painting is nevertheless a complete statement of Wang Hui's own achievements. He was now a successful master. Sadly, however, he was to enjoy success alone: while he himself lived on to die in his eighty-sixth year, in 1717, Wang Chien died in 1677, Wang Shih-min in 1680, and even his close friend and contemporary, Yün Shou-p'ing, in 1690. The painting of 1675 is thus the last to show here the effect of his friends' encouragement and that spirit of inquiry that had led him to such heights of accomplishment in his works of the late 1660s and early 1670s.

In 1691, two years after the K'ang-hsi emperor's tour of the South, Wang Hui was summoned to Peking to supervise the painting of the *Nan-hsün t'u*, a series of handscrolls describing and commemorating the emperor's journey. He remained at the capital until the work was finished in 1698, when he returned home to Yü-shan, bearing with him a signal mark of the emperor's commendation and favor: the inscription in the imperial hand *shan-shui ch'ing-hui*, "the landscape is clear and radiant," given to him in a personal audience. Thereafter, Wang Hui often used this phrase as one of his fancy names.

Wang Hui's appointment at the capital confirmed his position as the leading painter of the empire. A handscroll in the Morse Collection exemplifies the popular style which earned him many commissions. Entitled "Mountain Hermitage on a Clearing Autumn Day" (No. 19), it is dated 1692 and is based partly on the manner of the Yüan master Wang Meng and partly on that of Chao Meng-fu. The resemblance to the latter's "Autumn Colors on the Ch'iao and Hua Mountains," dated 1296, is particularly marked in the opening passages, where endless distant ranges of hills form the setting for a fishing village, and in the colors used throughout. The characteristics of Wang Meng's "dense and elegant" style may be seen in the lush scenery of the mountains and in the gigantic pine trees, the hallmark as it were, of a Wang Meng subject. Yet, Wang Hui is tied to no specific model, and his genius for lyrical beauty in landscape finds abundant expression. Throughout the handscroll the rhythms of the brushstrokes, repeated in the outlines of the rolling hills, in the vegetation dots that cover rocks and trees alike in rich and soft textures, give a unity to the whole and a clarity which is never lost even where the composition is at its most dense. This sure touch he retained to the very end of his life.

Many of Wang Hui's paintings from his time at court in Peking are magnificent in scale, like the undated "Winter Landscape" (No. 20) in the Morse Collection, a vast panorama of mountains and trees under a light covering of snow and a darkened sky. Others, from his last years, seem dry and terse by comparison with the freshness and vigor of his earlier masterpieces. They lack the resilience of the latter and show signs that he was now copying himself instead of reaching new heights with each new painting; yet they remain powerful in execution. The latest of Wang Hui's paintings in the Morse Collection, the handscroll of 1713 after Chü-jan and Yen Wen-k'uei, has all the marks of his final style—a certain grandeur and magnificence, obtained through the crystal-clear discipline of countless touches of the brush (No. 23). Wang Hui was conscious still of his power to raise heroic trees and great mountain ranges and to send the mighty clouds rolling to the furthest horizon.

VII

No one, in Wang Hui's old age, came near to occupying a place similar to that which he himself had enjoyed as the great hope and pride of Wang Shih-min and Wang Chien. Probably his greatest influence was upon his close friend Yün Shou-p'ing, who however died almost thirty years before him. Traditionally, Yün Shou-p'ing is supposed to have given up landscape painting, leaving the field to Wang Hui. This cannot have been entirely true, especially as regards landscapes on a small scale. However, two facts are clear: firstly, that Yün Shou-p'ing admired Wang Hui and wholeheartedly espoused the orthodox goals, as is clearly seen in his comments to the 1673 album; and secondly, that his landscapes generally—including that shown here (No. 26)—do not do justice to his unrivaled abilities as a flower-painter.

In the field of landscape painting, Wang Yüan-ch'i alone made a considerable contribution to the orthodox tradition (No. 27), yet he too, though ten years younger, was outlived by Wang Hui. A lesser figure, Yang Chin (1644-1728), worked with Wang Hui on the *Nan-hsün t'u* imperial commission, and is said to have painted figures and other details in many of the latter's paintings. His work in this exhibition (No. 28), dated 1726, is modeled closely on Wang Hui's final style, enlivened only by the addition of his own special motif of a boy with buffaloes. It is a fair sample of his work, which, though descriptive, seldom attains distinction. More originality, both in color and in surface texture, is evident in a landscape (No. 29) by Fang Shih-shu (1692-1751), a generation or more later. Here too the principles of abstraction and calligraphic brushwork, brought so thoroughly to perfection in practice by Wang Hui, are taken for granted as the chief means of painting a landscape. The result is fresh and attractive but lacks expressive strength.

With the exception of the late Ming garden painting bearing the seal of Wang Meng (No. 8) and the valuable replica of Wang Hui's important lost painting of 1672 after Chü-jan (No. 15), the paintings so far discussed are considered to be original works. There remain two paintings that belong to the category of forgeries, since they bear signatures and inscriptions of artists who clearly cannot have been their authors. Of these, the forgery of Wang Hui's work (No. 25) need detain us no longer than the mention of its presence: on grounds of quality alone it falls far below the standards that the master maintained to the end of his life. But a second forgery (No. 24) commands both interest and respect. This is a small hanging scroll with a brief inscription signed Ch'ih-weng, or Huang Kung-wang, and two of his seals. The calligraphy is in *ts'ao-shu* or draft style, quite unlike Huang Kung-wang's as we know it from the handscroll "Dwelling in the Fu-ch'un Mountains," but almost identical to Wang Hui's inscriptions on the leaves of his early undated album in the Palace Museum. Moreover, the brushwork of the landscape is extremely close to that of his painting of 1664 (No. 13) and to that of the sixth leaf and others in his album of 1673 in the Morse collection (No. 16). In short, this small landscape with the Huang Kung-wang inscription is almost certainly the work of Wang Hui, and probably dates from that period of the late 1660s and early 1670s in which, as we have seen, he produced the best work of his career. Evidently he expended no less energy and originality upon this piece than upon those signed with his own name. As Wang Shih-min wrote in 1661: "If a person judges Master Wang merely as excellent in making copies, he has missed the point by far."

Catalogue

of Numbers 1 through 29

by Roderick Whitfield

SHEN CHOU (1427-1509)

1   Autumn Colors among Streams and Mountains
Ch'i-shan ch'iu-se

Undated. Handscroll; ink on paper. Height: 0.198 m.; length: 6.402 m.

The handscroll opens with the title in four large characters by Shen Chou, with his signature and seals:

Autumn Colors among Streams and Mountains. Shen Chou inscribed.

The painting itself is on four sheets of paper, with inscriptions by Shen Chou and Yao Shou (1423-1495) on a fifth sheet of the same paper, all the joins being sealed with a seal of Shen Chou. His poem and explanatory note read as follows:

> It is more than a hundred years since Yün-lin [Ni Tsan] looked on the world
>   and painted it;
> What remain are only sparse trees, that look like old sparse ones.
> What are left for this old fellow to continue
> Are the long ranges piled up, with level wastes between them.

> This scroll was made to imitate Ni Yün-lin's conception. Yün-lin's methods were sparing, mine are cluttered. Yet though he was sparing, his meaning was ample. This is that which is known as the unlearnable.   Shen Chou.

Yao Shou wrote, probably on the same occasion:

> Not much ink but more than enough excitement [*hsing*]:
> [That is] old Ni's brushwork; his trees are plain and sparse.
> He only keeps a broken-down house, under the tall trees,
> Ridiculing the wastes of shattered tile among men.
>   Hsien-ch'ih, Yao Tzu-ho [Yao Shou].

50

I like paintings of mountains by Shen Shih-t'ien (Shen Chou) of Ch'ang-chou [Soochow]. Nowhere does he talk about their value, nor yet does he boast that his brush is as good as old Ni's; instead he lets himself go with an elegant poem, keeping close to Madman Mi [Mi Fu, 1051-1107]. In appreciation of Shih-t'ien.

Ch'ih [Yao shou].

Because the trees are sparse many rocks appear;
As the water is shallow it hides few of its pebbles.
Among men [this would be like] wine from Wu-ch'eng [i.e. *vin du pays*]
Or a plain board door in Chiang-nan.

I asked Shih-t'ien for an inscription.

In using ink he doesn't care if it is too pale; in pale [ink] the meaning is deep. Why are Tao-ning's [Shen Yeh-yün, a Taoist practitioner, active ca. 1405-1425] paintings so black, and not aloof like this?   I-shih [Yao Shou].

There are two later colophons: the first is by T'ao Keng (unidentified), who also wrote a label for the scroll:

Who continues the brush of 'plain Ni'?
Responding to his call, 'lean Shen' copies him.
Though the soughing sparse trees are like the old ones,
Yet the ideas of complexity and abbreviation speak of the difference.
The structure of the painting is lofy and difficult to grasp;
The autumn mountains are pale, almost disappearing.

He has inscribed a poem;
Yao I-shih's appreciation
is already here.

In the Tao-kuang reign, the year *kuei-wei* [1823], the first month, I borrowed Shih-t'ien's handscroll painting imitating Yün-lin, in the collection of Yüan-hsiang, and roughly added a stanza, asking for criticism.   T'ao Keng

51

The second is by the scholar Lo Chen-yü (1866-1940):

> Very few works have been preserved from Shih-t'ien's earlier years, but many survive from his later ones. This scroll was made in his middle late years. He himself says he is imitating Ni Tsan, but in fact he draws strength from Mei-tao-jen [Wu Chen, 1280-1354], and he has a source in Pei-yüan (Tung Yüan, tenth century) as well, for the four Yüan Masters [Huang Kung-wang, Wu Chen, Ni Tsan and Wang Meng] all derive from Pei-yüan. [This scroll,] sparse and excellent, is his masterpiece. Yün-tung [Yao Shou] was older than Shih-t'ien, so that their enjoying this together cannot be just empty boasting by Yao Shou. The year *i-mao* [1915] of the Hsüan-t'ung period, the old person of Wu-t'ing, Lo Chen-yü, looked at it and inscribed this record.

SEALS:

Shen Chou: *Chu-shih-t'ing* (C & W, p. 167, no. 7),[11] before title; *Shen Ch'i-nan*, before title; *Shih-t'ien* (C & W, p. 168, no. 22), after signature to title; *Shen*, on joins; *Shen-shih Ch'i-nan*, after inscription.

Yao Shou: *Kung-shou*, before his inscription; *Yün-tung I-shih* and *Chia-ho Yao shih*, after the inscription.

Hsiang Hung-tso (1798-1835): *Lien-sheng shen-ting*, after Yao Shou's inscription.

T'ao Keng: *T'ao Keng chih yin*, after his colophon.

Yamamoto Teijirō (1870-1937): *Tz'u Yüeh-chih yüan-t'ing shu-wu chien-ts'ang chen-chi*, *Shih-chia*, and *Kuei-yü Ch'ih-an* on title sheet; *Ch'ih-an* and *Lei-shan chen-shang* on painting; *Ch'ih-an shu-hua*, after Yao Shou's inscription; *Erh-feng ch'ing-shang*, on label and wrapper; *Shan-pen shih Hsiang-hsüeh shu-wu pin-ch'en-hou chih yin*, on wrapper; *Kuan tz'u chen-chi shih chüeh wei-che shen k'o-hsiao yeh*, on wrapper.

Mounter's seal: *Wu Wen-yü chuang*, at end of scroll.

Lo Chen-yü (1866-1940): *Lo Chen-yü yin* and *Lo Shu-yen*, both after his colophon.

Sun Yü-wen (active *ca.* 1856): *Wen* (C & W, p. 560, no. 3) and *Pan-ch'an san-su* (C & W, p. 560, no. 7) after Yao Shou's inscription.

Published by Yonezawa Yoshiho, *Kokka*, 1966, no. 894.

---

[11] Reference is made to seals recorded in Victoria Contag and Wang Chi-ch'üan's *Seals of Chinese Painters and Collectors of the Ming and Ch'ing Periods* (Hong Kong, 1966) only when the seal in question appears to be identical with one recorded in that work. Close resemblances are not noted.

Details 1 a, b

1 c. Detail, actual size

T'ANG YIN (1470-1523)

2   Landscape album.

> Undated. Eight album leaves (A-H) mounted as a handscroll, with title and colophon; ink and colors on silk. Average size of leaves: Height 0.320 m.; width 0.425 m.

The first page opening displays four striking characters written by Wen Cheng-ming (1470-1559), with his signature and seals:

> Ink Masterpieces by Liu-ju [T'ang Yin]. Cheng-ming.

Each of the following paintings bears a poem by T'ang Yin, and leaves 3 and 6 also carry poems by Wen Cheng-ming.

Leaf A:

> Hsün-yang need not be the end of the world,
> On both banks the wind is fresh among the flowering rushes.
> Who is the officer Po [Po Chü-i, 772-846]
> Listening to the *p'i-p'a* in mid-river by the bright moon?
>
>   T'ang Yin painted.

Hsün-yang was Po Chü-i's place of exile, from which he wrote the celebrated *P'i-p'a hsing*, on the sad occasion of saying farewell to a friend at the riverbank, their sadness increased by the lack of music to accompany the wine. As they were about to part, they heard the sound of a *p'i-p'a* across the river and were able to persuade the player to join them. She was a former beauty who put all the sadness of her life story into her playing.

Leaf B:

> Ten *li* of pines on a continuous encircling ridge,
> A small bridge leading to a place deep in shade.

57

Carrying my *ch'in*, I wish to pluck it and sing with friends,
I am carefree as the wind on the clouds, endlessly.

T'ang Yin of Chin-ch'ang [Soochow].

Leaf c:

The old trees are dense, covering the thatched cottage,
A blue sky stretches over rivers and lakes without end.
I sit quietly all day by the verandah—
You should know that my mind is not upon the fish.   T'ang Yin.

Autumn colors have come thickly to the thatched house.
In the morning patches of new frost can be seen on a few leaves.
The man of *tao* enjoys the flavor of his idleness—
When he awakes from his nap and spreads out his books,
the evening sun is bright.   [Wen] Cheng-ming inscribed.

Leaf d:

It is evening at the lonely temple on the empty mountain,
Autumn at the rickety bridge over the ancient chasm.
Worried, I rush on:
Where is there an inn that I can stay at?   T'ang Yin.

Leaf e:

Torrents of driving and flying rain:
Being fearful at heart, my road becomes more difficult.
Vaguely I make out a distant bank
And rejoice that it is Huang's home.   T'ang Yin.

Leaf f:

Wild water, a deserted house, an air of solitude;
In the depths of the hills but few guests come visiting.
Birds call, about to rest, as the clouds and mist darken,
A pair of autumn leaves fall in the west wind.   T'ang Yin.

The evening sun slowly declines along the river bank,
The west wind blows chilly over the lake waters.
This is the very place where a poet finds his poems,
A trace of mountain scenery falls on the man singing in the saddle.

[Wen] Cheng-ming inscribed.

Leaf g:

Among the red trees white clouds fly;
The slanting sun is cut off below the brown thatched eaves.
Here indeed is a carefree solitary place.

58

Since it is difficult to speak to you I make a painting for you.

T'ang Yin.

Leaf H:

The cold snow comes early in the morning with a biting north wind,
Ten thousand mountains are covered with jade *fu-jung* [white lotus].
Although deep in wine I still feel ice forming on my leg,
How is it then that there are footprints of a guest on the bridge
over the stream?   T'ang Yin of Chin-ch'ang [Soochow].

Colophon:

At the right are [works from] T'ang Tzu-wei's [T'ang Yin's] brush. Tzu-wei's ideas are lofty, his brush carefree ... [one or two characters missing] [so that] by his works he stands in a school of his own. I have not seen copies [of older compositions] by him before: this album alone does not come from his own ideas, following ancient men in its entirety, yet it is not stiff and slow, like those who frown and fail to make a transformation in their copies of ancient [paintings]. Truly, among all the gentlemen in China, there is none who can surpass him. In the Chia-ch'ing reign, the year *wu-tzu* [1528], the fourth month, Wen Cheng-ming wrote at Yü-ch'ing-shan-fang.

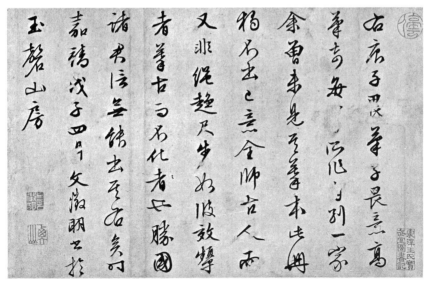

Wen Cheng-ming's colophon

59

T'ang Yin: *T'ang Tzu-wei*, leaves A, D; *Hsüeh-p'u-t'ang yin*, leaves A, C, D, F; *Liu-ju chü-shih*, leaves A, E; *Wu-ch'ü*, leaves B, C, G, H; *T'ang Po-hu*, leaves B, E, F, H; *T'ang Yin ssu-yin*, leaves B, G, H.

Wen Cheng-ming: *Wen Cheng-ming yin* (C & W, p. 636, no. 53) and *Heng-shan* (C & W, p. 20, no. 23), on title; *Cheng* and *Ming*, leaves C, F; *T'ing-yün*, before colophon; *Wen Cheng-ming yin* and *Heng-shan*, after colophon (different versions from seals used on title).

Ti Hsüeh-keng (early 20th century): *Li-yang Ti Hsüeh-keng tzu Man-nung i tzu Chia-sheng, Man-nung p'ing-sheng chen-shang*, on title leaf.

Unidentified: *Chung-shih-hsien, Shih-hao yü su ch'u suan hsien*, on title leaf; *Ch'eng-te* (Wu Ch'eng-te, unidentified), leaves A, D, E, F; *Wu Ch'eng-te yin* (*idem*), leaves B, C, G, H.

Wang Chi-ch'ien (C. C. Wang, born 1907): *Pao-wu-t'ang*, on title leaf, *Chen-tse Wang shih Chi-ch'ien so-ts'ang yin* and *Huai-yün-lou chien-shang shu-hua chih chi*, on mounting preceding leaf A; *Chi-ch'ien chen-ts'ang*, on each leaf.

The handscroll carries a label with the inscription:

A handscroll of poems and paintings by T'ang Po-hu of the Ming. *Shen-p'in* [divine class]. With a title and a record by Wen Heng-shan. The year *ting-hai* [1947], Hsüan-ko recorded.

潯陽未必是天涯兩岸
風清蘆荻花誰走舟中
由司馬滿江明月聽琵琶

唐寅畫

2 A

2 B

匹塢連岡十里松綠
陰深處小橋通橋
琴歌和吟邊社雲
上風騷不可窮

晉昌唐寅

古木深深覆草廬
江湖無際碧天鋪
臨軒盡日悠然坐
雅志應如不在魚
　寅

穗危雛到草堂平有
陳葉臨軒霜道个待
蕭閒晚晚撤書映夕
陽起　傲朋頓

2 C

2 D

蕭寺空山晚危橋古澗
秋愴惶行簇簇何慶
店堪接唐寅

2 E

2 F

2 G

2 H

Detail of 2 E, →
actual size

糧藉鸎飛雨
心危路轉餘寒
擡見遠浦惟喜
是黃家
唐寅

3   Album of scenes in the Cho-cheng-yüan (Garden of the Unsuccessful Politician), Soochow.

> Dated 1551. Eight painted leaves (A-H), with facing pages (AA-HH) inscribed with poems; ink on paper. Average measurements of paintings: height: 0.266 m.; width: 0.273 m.

Leaf AA:

> Various kinds of flowers are planted next to the thatched house:
> Purple luxuriance and red beauty in random array.
> The spring radiance and brilliance embroiders them with a thousand artifices;
> In the good air and scented mist a hundred fragrances mix.
> I love the odors that fill my bosom and sleeves,
> I do not heed the wind and dew that wets my clothes.
> My high thoughts are already beyond the noisy world.
> Aloof, I watch the bees flying up and down.
>
> The Fan-hsiang-wu [bank of many fragrances] is in front of the Jo-shu-t'ang. It is planted with a mixture of various kinds of peonies, begonias, wisteria and other flowers. Meng Tsung-hsien [act. ca. 1161-1190] said in a poem: "Beside your small house is a bank of many fragrances" [i.e. the name is taken from this poem].   Cheng-ming.

Leaf BB:

> Once a small pavilion was built by the Ts'ang-lang [pond];
> The green water still surrounds its empty railings.
> Here there are always wind and moon to offer to the fisherman,
> And boys, too, singing "Wash your hat tassels!"
> Rivers and lakes fill the whole land, enough for my enjoyment,
> For a hundred years the fish and birds have forgotten walls.
> Shun-ching [see below] is dead, Tu Ling [Tu Fu, 712-770] far away—
> As a paragon of hermits who will compete with me?
>
> The garden has several *mu* of water reservoirs, like Su Tzu-mei's [Su Shun-ching of the Sung dynasty, who had a Ts'ang-lang pavilion at Soochow] Ts'ang-lang ponds. So a pavilion was built amongst them, and called the lesser Ts'ang-lang. Formerly Tzu-mei returned from the capital, Pien. Our lord from Wu [i.e. the owner of the garden, Wang Hsien-ch'en, *chin-shih* in the Hung-chih reign, 1488-1505] also came back from the northern capital. The name is taken from this coincidence of their travels.

The name Ts'ang-lang is an allusion to retirement from government going back to a poem by Ch'ü Yüan, *Yü Fu* (The Fisherman), of which one couplet reads (in Professor Hawkes' translation):

> When the Ts'ang-lang's waters are clear, I can wash my hat-strings in them;
> When the Ts'ang-lang's waters are muddy, I can wash my feet in them.

Professor Hawkes notes: "The meaning is that you should seek official employment in good times and retire gracefully when the times are troubled."[12]

Leaf CC:

> Bamboos are planted around the low mound
> Forming a bank of bamboo around the edge.
> In full summer it already seems to be autumn,
> So deep is the wood, one cannot tell when it is noon.
> In its midst is one who has abandoned the world,
> Enjoying himself with a *ch'in* and a goblet.
> When a wind stirs he wakes too from drunkenness
> To sit and listen to the rain on the bamboo leaves.

The Hsiang-yün bank is south of the Peach-blossom rill and north of the Huai-yü pavilion. It is planted all around with bamboos and is especially quiet and secluded.   Cheng-ming.

Leaf DD:

> The new banana is more than ten feet tall;
> After rain it is clean as though washed.
> It does not dislike the high whitened wall,
> It elegantly matches the curved balustrade.
> Autumn sounds come into the cool pillow,
> Morning colors divide the green window.
> Let no one tell the heedless shears to take it,
> Leave it until the shade reaches the house.

The banana enclosure is to the left of the Huai-yü-t'ing. Later, palms were planted, to make a suitable shade for the summer months.   Cheng-ming.

Leaf EE:

> The white stone is clean and dustless;
> Flat, it overhangs the stream of wild water.
> I sit and watch the line rolling,

---

[12] David Hawkes: *Ch'u Tz'u: The Songs of the South* (Oxford, 1959), p. 91.

I take quiet pleasure in the jade-like turning [of the water].
I enjoy rivers and lakes, far off,
I forget cares, and terns and egrets become tame.
You must know that he who stretches his line,
Is not one who desires [to catch] fish.

The Fishing stone is below the I-yüan-t'ai [Pavilion of Distant Thoughts]. At the time of spring brightness, the shade of the willows and the falling flowers make one sit so absorbed as to forget to return.   Cheng-ming.

Leaf FF:

Here in summer a cool shade spreads over ten *mu*.
That is when the fruits begin to ripen in the long orchard.
At the place where the precious heavy baskets are divided and given away,
In a small window, I have got a rubbing of Yu-chün's [Wang Hsi-chih's] calligraphy.

The Lai-ch'in-yu [Garden to attract birds] consists of several hundred apple trees [*lin-ch'in*, literally "wood-birds"] planted on both sides of the Ts'ang-lang pond.

Leaf GG:

Once I ladled water from Hsiang-shan
Cool as a stream of jade.
Would you know that as far as Yao [7th star of the Dipper] is from
    the Milky Way
There is another clear jade spring?
Preparing a rope, I draw water with the clouds,
In an earthen jar, I boil it with moonlight.
What need of Lu Hung-chien [Lu Yü, a tea-taster in the T'ang]?
At the first sip you will yourself decide.

At Hsiang-shan in the capital there is a Jade spring, where the Master often ladled the water and made tea, and called himself Yü-ch'üan shan-jen [Hermit of the Jade spring] after it. When he struck a spring in the south-east corner of the garden, and the jar kept [its water] cold and suitable for tea, no less than that of the Jade Spring, he gave it this name, to show that he would not forget.   Cheng-ming.

Leaf HH:

Below the pavilion a tall locust tree falls over the wall,
Mist on the cold leaves wets my clothes.

The scattered flowers are sparse but their scent travels far,
The cool shade falls all around, of lasting benefit to the world.
The literary contests of the eighth moon recall past doings,
When the honors of the three ministers were entrusted to the candidates.
Since I became old I have not dreamt of Nan-k'o [of receiving high office],
Alone I move my bed to lie in the cool of the evening.

The Locust Pavilion, the year *hsin-hai* [1551], autumn, the ninth month, the 20th day.   Wen Cheng-ming wrote.

Colophons: The first is by Yung Hsing (1752-1823), eleventh son of the Ch'ien-lung emperor:

Heng-shan's [Wen Cheng-ming's] poems, at the time when the Ch'i-tzu [a literary group of seven scholars in the Chia-ching reign 1522-1567] were flourishing, along with those of Kuei Tzu-mu (*chin-shih* in the same reign) transcended the dusty world. In painting he studied the Wu-hsing style. In calligraphy also, though he was later, he does not yield much to the best of the earlier Ming period. This album, though a personal and lesser work, is of great interest for people to look into.

In the Tao-kuang reign, in winter, the 21st day.

    Ch'eng-ch'in-wang recorded, being at the time aged 70 [1801].

The second is by Naito Konan (1866-1934):

This album has paintings by the *tai-chao* Heng-shan of the complete views of the gardens and ponds of one surnamed Wu. The garden must originally have been well-known, but is so no longer now. The brushwork of the painting is marvellous; the ink is old and pale, similar to that of Tzu-ang and Chung-mu, father and son [Chao Meng-fu, 1264-1322, and his son Chao Yung]. Thus people enjoy looking at it and cannot bear to put it down, and it really is one of the most beautiful works among Heng-shan's paintings. For every leaf there is inscribed a poem, and at the end are the characters *hsin-hai*, namely the 30th year of the Chia-ching reign (1551), when Heng-shan was 82 *sui*. His calligraphy is slightly inferior to the painting. It has been in the family collection of the two nobles I-chin (Yung Hsing) and Hsi-chin (another son of the Ch'ien-lung emperor) of An-lu-ts'un, and it has a colophon by Ch'eng-wang (Yung Hsing). It should be treasured.

                        Showa, the fifth year (1930),
                        the eighth month, Naito Tora
                        (Naito Konan).

Wen Cheng-ming: *Wen Cheng-ming yin* (C & W, p. 636, no. 53) and *Heng-shan* (C & W, p. 20, no. 24), after each of his inscriptions; *Wen Cheng-ming yin*, another version, on the painting on leaf H; *Yü-lan-t'ang*, on leaf H.

Chang Hsiao-ssu (early 17th century): *Chang Tse-chih* (C & W, p. 570, no. 6), leaves A and H.

Chou Tso-hsin (received *chin-shih* degree in 1637): *Chou Tso-hsin yin* and *Mo-nung*, on leaf HH.

An Ch'i (1683-1742): *I-chou chen-ts'ang* (C & W, p. 536, no. 7), on all the paintings.

Chang T'ing-yü (1672-1755): *Ch'uan-ching-t'ang chen-ts'ang yin*, leaf HH.

Chang Jo-ch'eng (*chin-shih* 1745, son of Chang T'ing-yü): *Lien-hsüeh chien-ting*, leaf HH.

Yung Jung (1743-1790, sixth son of the Ch'ien-lung emperor): *Huang-liu-tzu* and *Kung-ch'in-wang*, leaf HH.

Yung Hsing (1752-1823, eleventh son of the Ch'ien-lung emperor): *I-chin-chai*, following his colophon.

Naito Konan (1866-1934): *Pao-ma an*, following his colophon.

Pao Hsi (late 19th century): *Shen An p'ing-sheng chen-shang* and *Pao Hsi ch'ang-shou*, on leaf HH.

Unidentified: *Yün-chen-ko t'u-shu chi* and *Ta-ming Ch'eng-shih Wei-an shang-chien t'u-shu*, on leaf HH.

In addition, the album is provided with a label by Ying Ho (1771-1840) written when it was in his collection (the En-fu-t'ang). It is recorded in *Tōan-zo shogafu* (Osaka, 1928), vol. 4, pls. 24/1-24/10.

3 AA 　3 A

雜植名花傍學堂 紫雞丹艷
傍成行盡堪隸隸楊之橋詩時
築董蕓薈百和香自愛芳蘇陽
傍袖不奈風霖湿右常高情
已上紫薈薷幽靜眷游醉上小
牡丹石蕅墅堂之前雜
植牡丹芍葉丹溴崇宏
楊詩花盡宗彤訪云修
君小葉燥奇鴗
澂明

3 BB 　3 B

傍澹泊楷小亭條墅孤小
遠君楷董無几月竹垂柯之
習沈童唱灌溉滿地江湖即
壽興夕平重亏己巨楊舞峩
已矣杜陵連一段出躂澂與弄
園書楂水楷巳乾頫顏薷子
美澂泊派彤因葉亭亏平曰
小澹派藚子美自派都彤吳
巻芳名澂泊董月北移鄒陵右叭榜
澂明

曾向青山中洽絃玉一
松寅知移浮陽到青玉泉
清帶便和雲汲沙辨来
月高日須陸临潮一啜自
分明东将青山青玉泉天
曾向西丘之困辨玉泉之人
及得泉於園主辨之别
里若石藏玉泉邈以為久
亦不辰紀
　　　　澂明

高八高桃芬表牆氣蒸
寒翠湿衣衣絲花鹿
流芳遠馮薩卉世泽长
日又橋懷性予三立然
業付諸防老未名作南
柯曹桐自楊林以晚凉
桃帷辛亥秋九月廿
　日　澂明書

Detail of 3 c, →
actual size

CH'IEN KU (1508-1574)

4 Gathering at the Orchid Pavilion
Lan-t'ing hsiu-hsi

Dated 1560. Handscroll; ink and colors on paper. Height: 0.238 m.; length: 4.36 m.

The handscroll begins with a title in four characters, written by Wang Ku-hsiang (1501-1568, *chin-shih* 1529):

Gathering at the Orchid Pavilion.

Ku-hsiang.

Following the painting Ch'ien Ku transcribed the full text of Wang Hsi-chih's account of the *Lan-t'ing hsü*, together with the poems written on the occasion and the names of the writers, the tally of poems written and of cups of wine drunk in forfeit. Following this fairly lengthy transcription is a colophon by Ch'ien Ku himself:

There are no less than several tens of versions of the Lan-t'ing document, together with its colophons and records, engraved on stone in ancient and modern times. Only the *ting-wu* version is considered fine. However, even the *ting-wu* version has fat and lean parts and is not uniformly governed, so that it is not known which one should prevail. The old abbot, the priest Ch'un-ning, takes delight in poetry and letters, and I used often to enjoy the arts in his company. Therefore, when we saw the engraved version at Prince Chou's house, he pasted together these three sheets of old paper and asked me to paint it. So I sat down, but in the course of the work, because of many settings-to and many layings-aside, it was five months before I was able to complete the composition of the picture. Then he again urged me to copy from the *ting-wu* version all the writings and verses and names at the end in order to make it complete and enjoyable. I, not being a student of calligraphy, refused, but he would not accept this, and I was forced to do it. I feel that my brush is clumsy and ugly, and my use of it common and vague. How dare I follow the men of old? I may only do so, in order that the painting and the writing may

76

be preserved together for the perusal and enjoyment of those who live in retirement in the mountains. If it is got out to show other people then my regrets and blame will be many. I am ashamed of my holding of the brush.

The time being in the Chia-ching reign, the year *keng-shen* [1560], the sixth month, the 15th day, Ch'ien Ku of P'eng-ch'eng recorded.

Colophon by Ch'ien Ku's son Yün-chih:

Over the generations there have been many engravings of the *Lan-t'ing* picture, large and small, and the rubbings from them are very fine. Nowadays among those that have been preserved and are still kept, the one engraved by I-fu is by far the finest, not to mention its influence; my ancestor made this scroll for Ping-hu Shang-tsu. Although it does not conform exactly to the original colors used in old examples, yet it has an airy beauty and a light radiance which fill the brush and silk, this is to be treasured. Now his grandson Chüeh-lin treasures it carefully wrapped in his collection; one can say that he is able to rejoice in keeping it. Several times he has taken it out to show me, and begged for a colophon, so I have written this.

In the year *chia-tzu* [1624] of the T'ien-ch'i period, the 2nd month, the 19th day, Ch'ing-ming, [Ch'ien Ku's] son Yün-chih respectfully recorded, being at the time aged 84.

SEALS:

Ch'ien Ku: On the right edge of painting: *P'eng-ch'eng* (C & W, p. 717, no. 17), also after post-face; *Ch'ien Ku* (C & W, p. 473, no. 5), also on two joins, before the inscriptions, and after the post-face; *Shu-pao* (C & W, p. 473, no. 4), also after the text of *Lan-t'ing hsü* and after the post-face; *Chü Wu i-min* (C & W, p. 474, no. 11), also before post-face.

On left edge of painting: *Ch'ien Ku ssu-yin* (C & W, p. 717, no. 20); *Shu-pao* (C & W, p. 717, no. 15); *Sang-tzu-li* (C & W, p. 717, no. 18); *Hsüan-ch'ing-shih hua yin* (C & W, p. 717, no. 20), also before inscriptions; *Hsüan-ch'ing-shih* (C & W, p. 474, no. 12).

Before inscriptions: *I-yüan-hsien* (C & W, p. 474, no. 22); *Ch'ien Shu-pao shih* (C & W, p. 717, no. 21), also after Ch'ien Ku's own colophon.

After text of *Lan-t'ing hsü*: *Meng-chih-chai* (C & W, p. 717, no. 19), also after post-face.

Before post-face: *Ch'ien Shu-pao* (C & W, p. 717, no. 23).

After post-face: *Wu Yüeh wang-sun* (C & W, p. 717, no. 24).

Before Ch'ien Ku's own colophon: *Yu-chu shan-ch'uang* (C & W, p. 717, no. 16).

Wang Ku-hsiang (1501-1568): *Yu-shih* (C & W, p. 64, no. 8), *Wang Lu-chih yin*

(C & W, p. 642, no. 16), and *Chien-pai-chai* (C & W, p. 64, no. 15), all after his signature on title.

Ch'ien Yün-chih (1541-c. 1620): *Ch'ien Yün-chih* and *Kung-fu*, after his inscription.

Ch'ien-lung Emperor (r. 1736-1796): *Shih ch'ü pao-chi* (C & W, p. 582, no. 31); *Ch'ien-lung yü-lan chih pao* (C & W, p. 582, no. 20); *Shih-ch'ü ting-chien* (C & W, p. 583, no. 41); *Pao-chi ch'ung-pien* (C & W, p. 583, no. 37); *Ch'ien-ch'ing-kung chien-ts'ang pao* (C & W, p. 583, no. 44); *Ch'ien-lung chien-shang* (C & W, p. 581, no. 12); *San-hsi-t'ang ching-chien hsi* (C & W, p. 583, no. 51); *I-tzu-sun* (C & W, p. 583, no. 39).

Chia-ch'ing Emperor (r. 1796-1820): *Chia-ch'ing yü-lan chih pao* (C & W, p. 578, no. 16).

Hsüan-t'ung Emperor (r. 1909-1912): *Hsüan-t'ung chien-shang; Wu-i-chai ching-chien hsi; Hsüan-t'ung yü-lan chih pao.*

Wang Chi-ch'ien (C. C. Wang, born 1907): *Chen-tse Wang shih Pao-Wu-t'ang t'u-hua chi*, on title; *Chen-tse Wang shih Chi-ch'ien so-ts'ang yin*, on brocade; *Huai-yün-lou chien-shang shu-hua chih chi*, on brocade; *Wang Chi-ch'ien hai-wai so-chien ming-chi*, end of the painting; *Ts'eng-ts'ang Wang Chi-ch'ien ch'u*, before the inscriptions.

The scroll is recorded in *Shih-ch'ü pao-chi, ch'ung-pien*. It entered the imperial collections probably in the middle of the eighteenth century and became separated from the main body of the collections after the fall of the Ch'ing dynasty in 1912. Ch'ien Ku's numerous seals on the scroll are all recorded in Contag and Wang, with many of them being entered from this scroll in the augmented edition published in 1966.

Ch'ien Ku's transcriptions of the *Lan-t'ing hsü* and of its accompanying records have not been translated here. A partial translation of the *Lan-t'ing hsü* itself is given by Arthur Waley (*An Introduction to the Study of Chinese Painting*, 1923, p. 70); it has also been translated by Lin Yu-t'ang (*The Importance of Living*, 1937, pp. 156-158).

Ch'ien Ku's transcription of Wang Hsi-chih's
account of the *Lan-t'ing hsü*.

Ch'ien Ku's colophon

LAN YING (1585-1664)

5   Red Friend
Hung-yu

> Undated. Hanging scroll; ink and colors on paper.
> Height: 1.482 m.; width: 0.474 m.

The painting bears a short inscription by the artist:

> Red Friend
> I painted this at the Shen-yen-t'ang.
> > Lan Ying.

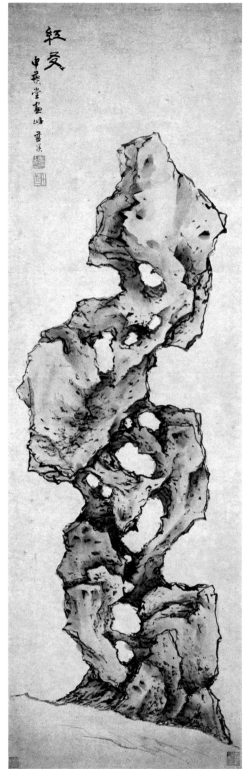

No. 5

No. 6

CH'EN HUNG-SHOU (1598-1652)

6 Landscape

Dated 1633. Hanging scroll; ink and colors on silk. Height: 2.356 m.; width: 0.778 m.
Inscription:

> The year *kuei-ch'ou* [1633], in mid-winter, Ch'en Hung-shou of Ch'i-shan wrote
> this at the Ch'i-fu-lou.

SEALS:

Ch'en Hung-shou: *Hung-shou* (C & W, p. 323, no. 3); *Chang-hou* (C & W, p. 323, no. 2).
This painting is recorded and described in Li Tso-hsien, *Shu-hua chien-ying* (1871), ch.
22, p. 11a.

No. 7

6 a. Detail of No. 6

CH'EN HUNG-SHOU (1598-1652)

7 Vase of Flowers.

Undated. Hanging scroll; ink and colors on silk. Height: 1.59 m.; width: 0.602 m.

Inscription:

Ch'en Hung-shou of Chi-shan painted at the Lao-t'ieh-hsien in Nan-feng.

SEALS:

Ch'en Hung-shou: *Ch'en Hung-shou yin; Chang-hou.*
Ch'eng Chi-i (Ch'ing dynasty): *Pao Sung-shih chien-ts'ang yin.*
Lin Yu-kuang (modern): *Lang-an so-ts'ang.*
Wu Ch'ing-tu (modern): *Wu Pi-ch'eng chien-ting yin.*
Unidentified: *Lai-su-lou.*

89

7 a. Detail of No. 7
actual size

WEN PO-JEN? (1502-1575)

Forgery of Wang Meng (1308-1385)

8   Landscape.

Hanging scroll; ink and colors on paper. Height: 1.031 m.; width: 0.499 m.

SEALS:

Wang Meng: *Huang-ho ch'iao-che.*

Hsiang Yüan-pien (1525-1590): *Tzu-ching chih yin* (C & W, p. 611, no. 32), lower right.

Ho Kuan-wu (contemporary Hong Kong collector): *Kuan-wu ching-shang, T'ien-ch'i shu-wo,* lower right.

Wang Chi-ch'ien (C. C. Wang, born 1907): *Chen-tse Wang shih Pao-wu-t'ang t'u-hua chi,* lower left.

Unidentified: *Yen-ju hsin-shang, Lin-hsia yeh-jen, Kang-chou Li shih Jih-tung chen-shang, Tzu-ch'un,* and *?-ch'i yin-chang,* on lower right corner; *Wu shih Yün-ch'in-kuan so-ts'ang shu-hua, Tzu-ting ssu-yin, Wu Po-tzu chen-ts'ang,* and *Ku-shan,* on lower left of painting.

The painting was exhibited in Canton in 1933 (*Kuang-chou-shih ti-i-tz'u chan-lan-hui,* p. 33). It was at that time in the collection of Ho Kuan-wu.

A copy of this painting, by Wang Hui, is in the Ku-kung collection, and is reproduced in William Cohn, *Chinese Painting* (London, 1948), pl. 214.

No. 8

No. 9

TUNG CH'I-CH'ANG (1555-1636)

9   Shaded Dwelling among Streams and Mountains
Ch'i-shan yüeh-kuan

> After Tung Yüan (10th century).

> Undated. Hanging scroll; ink on paper. Height: 1.586 m.; width: 0.72 m.

Inscription:

> Tung Pei-yüan's *Ch'i-shan yüeh-kuan* painting I once saw at the eunuch Chu's residence at Pei-fei. I made a sketch from it [and put it] in my cases. Now I have just completed this [painting] and it resembles [the original] rather well.
>
> Hsüan-tsai.

SEALS:

Tung Ch'i-chang: *Tsung-po hsüeh-shih; Tung Hsüan-tsai.*

Chang Ching (before 1861): *Chang Ching ssu-yin; Shen-ting chen-ts'ang.*

K'ung Kuang-t'ao (nineteenth century): *Yüeh-hsüeh-lou; Nan-hai K'ung Kuang-t'ao shen-ting chin-shih-shu-hua yin.*

K'ung Kuang-yung (nineteenth century): Kuang-yung ssu-yin.

Li Hui-han (modern): *Li wu-pen-t'ang ts'ang shu-hua chih yin; Li Tzu-yün shen-ting chang.*

Unidentified (contemporary Hong Kong collector): *Huang shih Huai-hsüan-t'ang ts'ang* (in yellow ink, a mourning seal for the collector's mother. The same seal is seen on a painting, No. 65, by Wen Po-jen in the Crawford collection, and on an album by Hung-jen in the Mu-fei collection, Cambridge).

K'ung Kuang-t'ao owned the painting in the mid-nineteenth century and recorded it in his *Yüeh-hsüeh-lou shu-hua lu* (preface dated 1861), ch. 4, p. 89b (1889 edition). At that time there were only two collectors' seals on the painting, those of Chang Ching on the above list.

WANG SHIH-MIN (1592-1680)

10   Landscape in the style of Huang Kung-wang (1269-1354).

    Dated 1666. Hanging scroll; ink on paper. Height: 1.433 m.; width: 0.562 m.

Inscription:

    Among the students who were listed with my grandfather Wen-su[13] on the honors list (of the *chin-shih* examinations) of the year *jen-hsü* [1562], very few of their descendants could write except for Mr. Yu Chu of Sung-ling, who alone deserved merit in letters and was famous in Chiang-tso [i.e. in Chekiang and Kiangsu]. I am honored to be in his company and I admire him very much. When he was young he wandered and did not settle, and when he became older he retired to the country where there was no way for me to make his acquaintance. In mid-autumn of the year *keng-tzu* [1660], because the monk Ling-yen moved to Hu-ch'iu in [Wu]-hsi, I had a chance to meet him at the abbot's place. We grasped hands and spoke of the past with as much pleasure as if we had known each other all our lives. During our conversation, he asked me for one of my stupid paintings. Thereupon I promised this, but then because I was transferred several times, and calamities contributed to fill my breast with anxiety, and illnesses all collected and bore down upon me, I did not keep my promise for six years, not doing anything in reply. Recently he wrote again to urge me and moreover sent me a work by his father. Receiving his favors and generosity increased my shame yet more, and one day when the clouds lifted and my window was clear, I forced myself to wipe my eyes and wash away the dust, and applied myself to copying Tzu-chiu's [Huang Kung-wang's] brush conception, making a small picture which I send, begging for correction. I laugh and am ashamed of this ugly thing; how can it be worthy to be presented for criticism? I remember that our ancestors were linked in the world of literature: at the best time they were as close as the mouth-pipe and the bamboo flute; they were of like mind as orchid and fragrant grass: how happy they were! Now of their heirs and grandsons there are only two of us left, both of us white-haired after grief, disturbance and

---

13 Posthumous title of Wang Hsi-chüeh, who was placed first in the examinations in the Chia-ching reign, 1522-1567, and who became a Han-lin scholar at the beginning of the Wan-li reign, 1573-1619.

← 9a. Detail of No. 9
actual size

No. 10

10a. Detail,
actual size

parting, and an excess of successive calamities. We were predestined to meet again. By means of brush and ink we express the thoughts of our hearts. How can this be accidental? Looking both at the times as they were then and as they are now, I cannot contain my sadness.

In the year *ping-wu* [1666], early in spring, the younger brother Wang Shih-min recorded, at the age of seventy-five.

SEALS:

Wang Shih-min: *Wang Shih-min yin* (C & W, p. 49, no. 8), and *Yen-k'o* (C & W, p. 49, no. 16), after inscription;[14] *Chen-chi* (C & W, p. 50, no. 38), before inscription.

Chang Ta-ch'ien (born 1899): *Ta-feng-t'ang chen-ts'ang yin; Nan-pei-tung-hsi chih-yu-hsiang-sui wu-pieh-li.*

Wang Po-yüan (late nineteenth century): *Po-yüan shen-ting.*

Wang Chi-ch'ien (C. C. Wang, born 1907): *Wang Chi-ch'ien hai-wai so-chien ming-chi.*

The painting is published in Sherman E. Lee, *A History of Far Eastern Art* (New York, 1964), fig. 586.

---

[14] These two seals, following Wang Shih-min's inscription, are recorded in Contag and Wang from this painting, at that time in the collection of Wang Po-yüan.

WANG CHIEN (1598-1677)

11   Landscape in the style of Huang Kung-wang.

   Dated 1657. Hanging scroll; ink on paper. Height: 1.15 m.; width: 0.562 m.

Inscription: The mountain mists wind about and the roads cross too;
         Recently I built a rush hut, narrow but still beautiful.
         With my own hands I planted pines and firs, all old and large.
         For a whole year I have not trodden the gates and streets of the town.

   In the winter of *ting-yu* [1657], imitating Ta-ch'ih's [Huang Kung-wang's]
   painting of "Autumn Mountains."   Wang Chien.

                         SEALS:

Wang Chien: *Pao-chih-lou*, before inscription; *Wang Chien chih yin* (C & W, p. 82, no.
   13), after inscription.
Forged imperial seals: *San-hsi-t'ang* and *Nei-fu t'u-shu*, upper right; *Mao-ch'in-tien
   chien-ting chang*, upper center; *Shih-ch'ü pao-chi, Chi-hsia i-ch'ing, Ch'ien-lung
   yü-wan*, and *I-tzu-sun*, upper left.
Ho K'un-yü (early nineteenth century): *Ho shih yü Yüan-ssu-chia hua-lou chih yin*,
   upper right; *Te-che pao-chih shu-ch'üan chiu-yüan*, and *Ho K'un-yü yin*, lower
   right.
Ho Yüan-yü (early nineteenth century): *Ch'ü-an p'i-ai pu-chia pu-shih*, upper right;
   Tuan-ch'i Ho shih Ch'ü-an so-ts'ang i-shih wu-liang, lower right.
Ch'in Tsu-yung (1825-1884): *Liang-ch'i Ch'in Tsu-yung chien-Shang chen-chi*, lower
   left.
Unidentified: *Ku-shang Huang Chün-yüan Tzu-lin shih so-ts'ang ming-jen tzu-hua chih
   chang*, lower left.

An inscription inside the box lid reads:

   Feng-ch'ang's [Wang Shih-min's] and Lien-chou's [Wang Chien's] paintings both derive from Ta-ch'ih [Huang Kung-wang]; they have established
   the style of [the Ch'ing dynasty's] 300 years. This painting by Lien-chou imitates Ta-ch'ih, and its spirit is very close to him. In discussing the orthodox
   tradition of Ch'ing painting one must begin with this rank. That it entered
   the Shih-ch'ü [the imperial Ch'ien-lung collections], that it was owned and
   enjoyed by Ho K'un-yü, and that Mr. Tung An[15] treasured and loved it, is
   possible. Tora [Naito Konan, 1870-1937] recorded. The year *wu-ch'en*
   [1928], the fourth month.

The painting is recorded in *Tōan-zō Shōgafu* (Osaka, 1928), vol. 4, pl. 44, when it was in
the Saito collection.

[15] Tung An, or Tōan: Saitō Etsuzō, nineteenth- to early twentieth-century Japanese collector.

峰嵐層曲性又加敬作
李堂宮太佳手程松杉
嘗光大經年不端孫門
術
丁酉先似大飛林
山閣 王敏

No. 11

11 a. Detai
actual size

山
川
渾
厚

草
木
華
滋

庚
子
春
做
子
久

筆
意
為

毓
翁
老
先
生
壽

王
翬

No. 12

WANG HUI (1632-1717)

12   Landscape in the style of Huang Kung-wang.

Collection of The Art Museum, Princeton University (69-70). Gift of Mr. and Mrs. Earl Morse in honor of Prof. and Mrs. Wen Fong.

Dated 1660. Hanging scroll; ink on paper. Height: 1.74 m.; width: 0.896 m.

Wang Hui's inscription in the upper right corner reads:

Mountains and streams round and full;
Grass and trees resplendent and lush.

The year *keng-tzu* [1660], winter, imitating the brush manner of Tzu-chiu [Huang Kung-wang]. [Painted] for the venerable Yü, for the old gentleman's birthday.   Wang Hui.

Mounted above the painting is an inscription written on brocade by the twentieth-century painter, connoisseur and collector Wu Hu-fan:

The True Heritage of Ch'ih-weng [Huang Kung-wang]. Chang Chü-ch'ü [Chang Yü, 1277-1348] inscribed a painting by Huang-ch'ih [Huang Kung-wang] with the words: "Mountains and streams round and full; Grass and trees resplendent and lush." The two Wangs of Lou-tung [Wang Shih-min and Wang Chien] spent their entire lives in study, that they might transmit the true tradition. When Shih-ku-tzu [Wang Hui] was a young man he served his teachers, the two Wangs, and received from them all of the secrets [of painting]. [In his art,] both the form and the spirit are complete. This painting is a copy by Shih-ku, at the age of 29 *sui*, of Hsiang-pi's [Wang Chien's] composition in the style of Ch'ih-weng. Not only are the brush and ink used with great skill, but if it were placed among Hsiang-pi's paintings of his middle years there would not be [seen] the slightest difference. The year *wu-yin* [1938], on a winter day, elder brother Sun Pang-shui, having newly acquired [this painting], showed it to me: I am delighted that it has found its rightful home, and have therefore recorded its origins.

Wu Hu-fan examined and inscribed.

SEALS:

Wang Hui: *Mo Ch'an* (C & W, p. 643, no. 95), before his inscription; *Wang Hui chih yin* and *Shih-ku*, after his inscription; *Shang-hsia ku-chin* (C & W, p. 69, no. 89), lower right corner.

Sun Pang-shui (twentieth century): *Pang-shui chien ts'ang* and *Chi-yang Sun shih*, in lower left corner.

Wu Hu-fan (twentieth century): *Hu-chün hsü yüeh, lower right corner*; *Wu Hu-chün yin*, after his inscription.

The name Yü in Wang Hui's inscription is a replacement, the original name, as often happens, having been erased probably when the painting was first sold, to avoid embarrassment to the family of the gentleman originally honored. The history of the painting prior to 1938, when it was owned by Sun Pang-shui, has not been ascertained.

WANG HUI

13   Landscape in the style of Chü-jan (active ca. 960-980).

Dated 1664. Hanging scroll; ink on paper. Height: 1.31 m.; width: 0.655 m.

Wang Hui's inscription, in the upper right corner, reads:

> Mountains and streams round and full;
> Grass and trees resplendent and lush.

The year *chia-shen* [1664], spring, imitating the brushwork of Chü-jan, [painted] for the venerable Hsiu on the old gentleman's birthday.

Wang Hui.

Above the painting, Wu Hu-fan has inscribed the following encomium:

> Light transmitted from Huang-ho [Wang Meng, d. 1385].
> This painting's brush method [derives] from Wang Shu-ming [Wang Meng], and has its eventual origin in Chü [-jan], the Master. Therefore its "breath and soul" is heroic and full. It is worthy of being praised as Ch'ing-hui's [Wang Hui's] masterpiece [*chia-kuan*].   Wu Hu-fan inscribed.

SEALS:

Wang Hui: *Wang Hui* (C & W, p. 68, no. 75), after his inscription; *Shang-hsia ku-chin* (C & W, p. 69, no. 89; both seals recorded from this painting, misdated 1700), lower left.

Wu Hu-fan (twentieth century): *Mei-ching shu-wu*, before his encomium and *Wu Hu-chün*, after it.

Wang Chi-ch'ien (C. C. Wang, born 1907): *Wang shih Chi-ch'ien chen-ts'ang chih yin*, lower right.

The venerable Hsiu, for whom Wang Hui did the painting, has not been identified. Before entering the Morse Collection, the painting was owned by Wu Hu-fan and C. C. Wang. In 1956 it was exhibited in the Loan Exhibition of Chinese Paintings, Royal Ontario Museum of Archaeology, Toronto, and reproduced in the catalogue, p. 48.

105

← 12a. Detail of No. 12
actual size

山川渾厚
草木華滋
甲辰春倣巨然筆為
脩翁老先生壽 王翬

No. 13

13 a. Detai
actual size

WANG HUI

14   The Colors of Mt. T'ai-hang
T'ai-hang-shan-se

>Dated 1669. Handscroll; ink and colors on silk. Height: 0.253 m.; length: 2.094 m.

Wang Hui's inscription, near the beginning of the painting, reads:

>Once at Kuang-ling, in the home of a noble family, I saw a small scroll by
>Kuan T'ung [ca. 907-950], "Cloudy Peaks Racing Together." In spirit it was
>luxuriant and dense, truly, it might "pierce the heart and startle the eye."
>Even today, I remember one or two tenths of it: accordingly I have imitated
>its method and made this "Colors of Mt. T'ai-hang." [The painting] must
>have the deep and heroic atmosphere of the Northern land, and not become
>attractive with pretty details. The year *chi-yu* [1669], three days after the
>mid-autumn festival, Wang Hui of Yü-shan [made] and inscribed [this
>painting].

To the right of Wang Hui's inscription, Wang Shih-min wrote the four characters of the
title in *pa-fen* style:

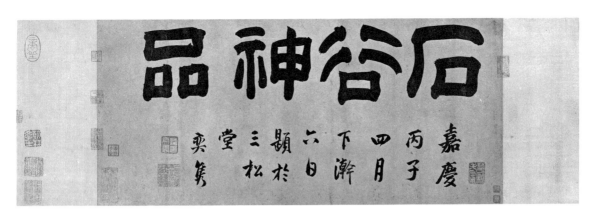

The Colors of Mt. T'ai-hang.

The year *kuei-ch'ou* [1673], late spring, Wang Shih-min enjoyed [this painting] and therefore titled it.

Mounted before the painting is a title inscription in large characters by an early nineteenth-century owner, P'an I-chün (1740-1830) himself a painter as well as a calligrapher:

Shih-ku shen-p'in, [Painting of the] Divine Class by Shih-ku [Wang Hui].

In the Chia-ch'ing [reign], the year *ping-tzu* [1816], fourth month, third decade, sixth day, inscribed at San-sung-t'ang ["Hall of the Three Pines," P'an's studio]. [P'an] I-chün.

Two colophons by Ch'en Ch'ung-pen (*chin-shih* in 1775) are attached to the end of the scroll. The first reads:

Fan Chung-li's [Fan K'uan, ca. 990-1030] large hanging scroll, *Hsüeh-shan hsing-lü* ["Travelling in Snowy Mountains"], which I once owned, has long since entered the *Shih-ch'ü pao-chi* [Imperial Collection]. Its brushwork and that of this scroll are extremely similar. One may thus know that in his breast Keng-yen [Wang Hui] had deeply attained the hills and valleys of the ancient men. Therefore, when he put his brush [to silk, the result was] like this, extremely full. At the beginning is a title by Hsi-lu-lao-jen [Wang Shih-min], from which one may gather his delight in it. [Ch'en] Ch'ung-pen recorded.

Ch'en Ch'ung-pen's second colophon follows:

I recently obtained some imitations of the ancients by Keng-yen [Wang Hui], four paintings [each measuring] about three feet square. Perhaps he intended them for a small standing screen showing the four seasons, but the silk, after more than a hundred years, has not yet been mounted. For the painting of the autumn scene he employed the sketch for this "Colors of Mt. T'ai-hang." I shall mount [the four paintings] on two hanging scrolls to preserve them for my enjoyment.
In the Chia-ch'ing [reign], the year *i-hai* [1815], seventh month, second day, recorded. [Ch'en] Ch'ung-pen.

Wang Hui: *Shih-ku* (C & W, p. 67, no. 2), and *Ch'en Hui* (C & W, p. 67, no. 11), both
after his inscription, and recorded in C & W from this painting.

Wang Shih-min (1592-1680): *Wang Shih-min yin* and *Yen-k'o* (C & W, p. 49, no. 5),
after his inscription; *Hsi-lu-lao-jen* (C & W, p. 49, no. 24) and *Yen-k'o chen-shang*
(C & W, p. 49, no. 26), at end of painting.

Wang Wen-po (active c. 1662-1722): *Ku-hsiang-lou ts'ang-pao* and (?) *Hai-t'i shen-ting
chen-chi*, at end of painting; *Hai-t'i shou ting*, after title.

Ch'en Ch'ung-pen (*chin-shih* 1775): *Po-kung so ts'ang*, after his first colophon; *Ch'ung-
pen p'ing-sheng chen-shang*, after his second colophon; *Shang-ch'iu Ch'en Ch'ung-
pen k'ao ts'ang yin*, left of title; *Shang-ch'iu*, on mounting before painting.

P'an I-chün (1740-1830): *Hua-ch'iao lao-p'u*, before title; *P'an I-chün yin* and *I hu mu-
lan liang teng T'ai-tai tsai yu Huang-hai san-su Wu-t'ai*, after title.

Hsü Nai-p'u (*chin-shih* 1820): *K'an-hsi-chai*, at end of painting; *T'ien-sheng so ts'ang*,
at end of painting and left of title; *K'an-hsi-chai shu-hua yin*, before and after title,
and again left of Ch'en Ch'ung-pen's first colophon; *T'ien-sheng Nai-p'u*, left of
title; *Ch'en Hsü Nai-p'u*, on joint at beginning of painting.

Ch'en K'uei-lung (*chin-shih* in the Kuang-hsü reign): *Ch'en Shao-shih hsin-hai hou
chien ts'ang*, at end of painting, right-hand column; *Han-lin hsüeh-shih* and *?-hsien
pi-chi chih yin*, both on mounting at beginning of painting.

Chang Ta-ch'ien (born 1899): *Ta-feng-t'ang chen ts'ang yin*, at beginning of painting;
Nan-pei-tung-hsi chih yu hsiang-sui wu pieh-li, at end of painting; *Ta-ch'ien hsi*
and *Chang Yüan*, before title.

Wang Chi-ch'ien (C. C. Wang, born 1907): *Wang Chi-ch'ien hai-wai so-chien ming-chi*,
on mounting at beginning of painting.

Unidentified: *Shih-t'ang chen wan*, below Wang Shih-min's title; *Yü shih so ts'ang* and
I-tzu-sun, at end of painting.

The handscroll seems to have been first owned by Wang Shih-min, and thereafter by
Wang Wen-po (active in the K'ang-hsi reign), the Yü family (not identified), Ch'en
Ch'ung-pen (*chin-shih* in 1775), P'an I-chün (1740-1830), Hsü Nai-p'u (*chin-shih* in
1820), Chang Ta-ch'ien (born 1899), Wang Po-yüan (in whose collection it was when
Wang Hui's seals from it were recorded in Contag and Wang, 1940), and C. C. Wang.
It is recorded in Chang Ta-yung, *Tzu-i-yüeh-chai shu-hua lu* (preface dated 1832),
chüan 4, p. 18; and in Ch'en K'uei-lin (late nineteenth century), *Pao-yü-ko shu-hua lu*,
chüan 2, p. 20.

15   Imitating Chü-jan's "Mist Floating on a Distant Peak"
      Fang Chü-jan Yen-fou yüan-hsiu t'u

        Dated 1672. Hanging scroll, ink on silk. Height: 1.93 m.; width: 0.715 m.

This painting is considered to be a very early replica of Wang Hui's painting of this subject, which has not been found. The colophons also are copied, but since there is no rea-
son to doubt the authenticity of their texts, they are referred to here as if written by
their respective authors.

Wang Hui's first inscription, to the left of top center, begins by transcribing the Sung
emperor Hui-tsung's (r. 1101-1126) title from the original painting by Chü-jan (active
ca. 960-980):

        Chü-jan's "Mist Floating on a Distant Peak." Title by Sung Hui-tsung.

Wang Hui then continues:

> [Chü-jan's] hanging scroll, famous throughout the land, is in the collection of
> the T'ai-shih Chuang Tan-an of P'i-ling. If any work may be compared with
> Pei-yüan's [Tung Yüan, active ca. 937-962] *Lung-su chiao-min t'u*, and be
> worth a thousand pieces of silver, then this is the one. The Shih-yü [Censor]
> Chiang-shan [Ta Chung-kuang, 1623-1692] and I had the good fortune of
> seeing it in the autumn of the year *jen-tzu* [1672]. Chiang-shan, an expert
> connoisseur, asked me to imitate it. Although my clumsy brushwork cannot
> compare with that of the ancient master, in structure and spirit-resonance I
> have managed to approximate it.   Wu-mu-shan-hsia-jen, Wang Hui.

In the upper right corner is an inscription by Wang Shih-min:

> Chü-jan's "Mist Floating on a Distant Peak" I had longed for all my life but
> had never set eyes on. In the autumn of the year *hsin-hai* [1671] I finally saw
> it in the Cho-cheng-yüan. Unfortunately, it was like Ch'ing-hsi's meeting with
> Buddha, for after seeing it once, I never saw it again. Towards the end of the
> year *jen-tzu* [1672], brother Shih-ku [Wang Hui], on his way back from
> Ching-k'ou, turned his boat aside to pay me a visit. He told me that he had
> made a copy for the Censor Tsai-weng [Ta Chung-kuang]. He happened to
> have the painting in his bag and brought it out to show me. As I unroll and
> examine it, I find the ink lustrous and brilliant, and a *yüan-ch'i* [primal breath]
> filling the composition. A feeling of joyful exhilaration moves freely in it, and
> the texture strokes are divinely inspired. Since [this painting] has already

opened a new life for Master Chü, why should I want the original? Shih-lao [Wang Hui] is certainly an artist whose craft competes with creation itself; yet without Tsai-weng's connoisseurship and deep friendship, how could such a masterpiece be produced? For myself, aged and infirm, the very opportunity to exclaim over such a scroll may be considered a remarkable coincidence. Thus I especially inscribe this above the painting to mark an important event in the history of art and also to note my own good fortune.

An eighty-one-year-old man of Lou-tung, Wang Shih-min.

In the upper left corner is an inscription by Wang Chien:

When Chuang Tan-weng [Chuang Tan-an] first acquired [the original] painting by Chü-jan, he especially brought it to Wu-men to show me. That was nearly twenty years ago. I have often seen it in my dreams. This winter brother Shih-ku [Wang Hui], on his way through Lou[-tung], showed me this scroll, which he has made for the Censor Tsai-weng. In its distant and subtle effects it almost surpasses the original. Even though the brilliant metamorphosis of the brushwork comes from Wang Hui's natural gifts, might he not have tossed away this *yeh-kuang* [pearl that glows in the night] had he not met Tsai-weng's discerning eye? I would like to congratulate myself privately on encountering three great happy events in one day: I have actually seen a living incarnation of Chü-jan; I have admired at a distance the cultured air of Tsai-weng; and I have come into close contact with Shih-ku's personal manner. At the close of the year, impoverished and sorrowed, to obtain this suffices to comfort me.   Inscribed by Wang Chien of Jan-hsiang-an.

Below Wang Chien's inscription is a second notation by Wang Hui:

This painting by Chü-jan does not make use of any paths, stream mouths, buildings, boats or bridges. It depends solely on broad and heroic *shih* [compositional forces]. Deep in the mountains where even woodcutters and shepherds do not reach, one often encounters true scenery such as this. This is the real style of Master Chü. It may be termed a work of the *i-p'in* [untrammeled class].

New Year's day of the year *kuei-ch'ou* [1673], Wang Hui made a second record.

SEALS:

Wang Hui: *Wu-mu shan-ch'iao*, before his first inscription; *Yu ho pu k'o*, after the Hui-tsung title; *Wang Hui chih yin* and *Tzu Shih-ku*, after his first inscription; *Wang Hui chih yin*, another version, after his second inscription.

Wang Shih-min (1592-1680): *Chen chi*, before his inscription; *Wang Shih-min yin* (C & W, p. 49, no. 8) and *Yen-k'o*, after his inscription.

Wang Chien (1598-1677): *Lang-yeh* (C & W, p. 82, no. 14), before his inscription; *Wang Chien chih yin*, following his inscription.

Unidentified: *T'a-t'a?-la shih chia-ts'ang*, lower right; *Kan-ch'u chen ts'ang*, lower left.

On the cover of the box now encasing the scroll is a label written by Naito Konan (1866-1934):

> Wang Shih-ku's copy of Chü-jan's "Mist Floating on a Distant Peak."
> Inscribed by Naito Tora.

The same collector has added a note inside the cover:

> This is a copy of Chü-jan's "Mist Floating on a Distant Peak" done for Ta Chiang-shang [Ta Chung-kuang] by Wang Shih-ku in his early years. Master Chü's original painting entered [the collection of the Northern Sung emperor Hui-tsung and is recorded in] the *Hsüan-ho hua-p'u*. This scroll moreover has been examined and appreciated by Feng-ch'ang [Wang Shih-min] and Lien-chou [Wang Chien]. It should be declared a rare sight and a great work. Its *ts'un* texture strokes and washes are loose and rich. The method of painting trees is deep and full-bodied. In it one sees the spirit and bearing of a great master.
> Inscribed in the fifth month of the year *wu-ch'en* [1928] by Naito Tora.

Before entering the Morse collection, the painting was in the Saito collection, Osaka, Japan. It is published in the catalogue, *Tōan-zō Shōgafu* (Osaka, 1928), vol. 4, pl. 47.

No. 15

WANG HUI

16   Album of landscapes after Sung and Yüan masters.

>   Dated 1673. Twelve painted leaves (A-L), nine in ink on paper, and three in ink and
>   colors on paper, with facing pages (AA-LL). With mounting, the album measures
>   0.314 m. in height, and 0.484 m. in width. The measurements of individual paintings
>   vary slightly; they are given in the description of each leaf.

Inside the brocade cover is a notation by a nineteenth-century owner, Shen Ping-ch'eng
(1823-1895):

>   Twelve leaves painted by Keng-yen-san-jen [Wang Hui] as a gift for Yen-
>   k'o Feng-ch'ang [Wang Shih-min]—small works after Sung and Yüan.
>   Yen-k'o personally inscribed the two characters, *Ch'ü Ku*, "In Pursuit of An-
>   tiquity," on one leaf.
>   Yün Nan-t'ien (Yün Shou-p'ing, 1633-1690) inscribed successive leaves.
>   Ta Chiang-shang (Ta Chung-kuang, 1623-1692) and other noted men, eleven
>   in all, wrote inscriptions.
>   Recorded by T'ieh-yen-lu [Shen Ping-ch'eng].

On the lower page of the first double leaf is a title by an eighteenth-century owner, Pi
Lung (active 1736-1796):

>   Authentic works by Wang Keng-yen after Sung and Yüan [masters], pre-
>   sented to Master Yen-k'o.

On the next double leaf are the two characters, *Ch'ü Ku*, "In Pursuit of Antiquity," written in the *pa-fen* style by Wang Shih-min, and his signature, Shih-min.

Leaf AA:

Colophon by Ta Chung-kuang:

>   Too lazy to imitate Yang Hsiung's [55 B.C.-A.D. 18] *Chieh-ch'ao* ["Apology"],
>   Burning incense, I muse over the diagrams of the "Changes."
>   Cares of the world touch not my place of leisurely rest,
>   The blue mountains are my only faithful friends.
>   Written for Master Yen-weng's [Wang Shih-min's] correction.
>   [Ta] Chung-kuang.

Leaf A:

Landscape in the style of Chü-jan (active ca. 960-980). Ink on paper. Height: 0.219 m.; width: 0.31 m.

Leaf BB:

Colophon by Ta Chung-kuang:

> A bamboo mat is perfect for a clear day,
> My light robe lets in a cold breeze;
> Had he not taken the gold on the road,
> How could Yen-ling have known Ch'iu Kung?
>
> Yü-kang-sheng inscribed.

Leaf B:

Landscape in the style of Tung Yüan (active ca. 937-962). Ink and slight color on paper. Height: 0.219 m.; width: 0.316 m.

On the mounting to the right of the painting is an inscription by Yün Shou-p'ing:

> Opening to this leaf, I suddenly find myself in a lonely and uninhabited world of wild cliffs and deep valleys. The trees cast somber shadows, while mountain torrents and paths wind their way around them. The scene fills less than one foot [ch'ih], yet one can roam in it with endless enjoyment. [A painter] must concentrate his spirit, reflect in solitude, cleanse [his mind] and emit a supernatural breath [so that] the powers of his miraculous brush may describe flavors beyond outward appearances, or he will not easily achieve such excellence. Shih-ku-tzu [Wang Hui] painted for Master Yen-weng [Wang Shih-min] this small scene in the style of Pei-yüan [Tung Yüan]. Truly, the metamorphosis is divine and brilliant. It is a masterpiece of the first order. Shou-p'ing inscribed.

Leaf CC:

Colophon by Ta Chung-kuang:

> The sky is blue, the clouds white, the trees deep deep green.
> A grass hut, a sparse fence, beside a wild bank;
> A pair of herdboys firmly astride their buffaloes,
> Playing their flutes in the glow of the setting sun.
> Written for Master Yen-weng [Wang Shih-min] to raise a laugh.
>
> Chung-kuang.

Leaf c:

Buffalo and herdboy, in the style of Li Ti [12th century]. Ink and slight color on paper. Height: 0.176 m.; width: 0.298 m.

To the right of the painting is a poem by Liu Yü (active ca. 1662-1722):

> The willows first touched with green
> Rustling far from the water village.
> The east wind wafts along as it will,
> Not lingering about the Ch'ang-men palace.[16]
>
> Liu Yü.

Leaf dd: Blank.

Leaf d:

Landscape in the style of Huang Kung-wang (1269-1354). Ink on paper. Height: 0.218 m.; width: 0.31 m.

To the right of the painting is an inscription by Yün Shou-p'ing:

> In the style of Ch'ih-weng [Huang Kung-wang] the location of peaks and valleys can be learned with success, but beyond the brush and ink there is also a certain rustic and hoary feeling which cannot be successfully learned. This is why in studying Ch'ih-weng one frequently falls short of attaining excellence. Only Master Feng-ch'ang of Lou-tung [Wang Shih-min] and Master Shih-ku of Yü-shan [Wang Hui] have been able to reach this degree. Shou-p'ing respectfully records this.

To the left of the painting is an inscription by Ch'en Ch'eng (latter half of the seventeenth century):

> In love of brush and ink we are of one heart;
> When busy our thoughts visit, at leisure we seek each other.
> Deep into the night, by a shaded lamp, I watch you painting,
> I know not whence comes that limpid sound.
> Inscribed on a small scene after Ch'ih-weng by Wu-mu-shan-jen [Wang Hui]. Ch'en Ch'eng of Chin-ling [Nanking].

---

[16] The Ch'ang-men Palace has symbolized the sorrow of separation since Ssu-ma Hsiang-ju (179-117 B.C.) wrote his *Ch'ang-men Fu* describing the sorrow of the Empress Ch'en at her separation from the Han emperor Wu (r. 140-87 B.C.).

Leaf EE: Blank.

Leaf E:

Landscape in the style of Ts'ao Chih-po (1272-1355). Ink on paper. Height: 0.216 m.; width 0.31 m.

To the right of the painting is a colophon by Yün Shou-p'ing:

> Shih-ku-tzu [Wang Hui] imitating the bamboo, rocks and dead branches of Yün-hsi [Ts'ao Chih-po]. He has a fresh and spirited flavor that one may enjoy without tiring. There is a saying that "even in a spoonful of water there are curves; even in a chip of stone there are hollows." This painting has obtained that quality.   Yün Shou-p'ing inscribed.

Leaf FF:

Colophon by Ta Chung-kuang:

> After the rain, spring bamboo fills the forest,
> There are also cherries, every one of them round.
> I believe that in the mountains even the wind tastes better,
> It makes me sad to think about the feast of the five lords.[17]
>> Written to be corrected by Master Yen-weng [Wang Shih-min]. Chung-kuang.

Leaf F:

Landscape in the style of Wang Meng (d. 1385). Ink on paper. Height: 0.214 m.; width: 0.331 m.

To the right of the painting are two colophons by Yün Shou-p'ing:

> When painting, one should sit cross-legged with loosened clothing, as if no one were around. Only then will one hold the powers of metamorphosis in one's hand, and the *yüan-ch'i* [primal breath] will abound. Unfettered by earlier masters, one will then be able to roam beyond the established rules. Shou-p'ing inscribed.

> I judge that this painting by Wu-mu Wang shan-jen [Wang Hui] after Shu-ming [Wang Meng] is truly enough to frighten away the flock of common painters. It is a treasure that pierces the heart and startles the eye. Inscribed again on the following day.

---

[17] Five members of the Wang family enfeoffed by the emperor Ch'eng of Han (r. 32-5 B.C.) were constantly quarreling, but at a feast to which all were invited their host succeeded in resolving one of their disputes. After watching them fight over choice delicacies, he threw everything into a pot and cooked it together.

Leaf GG:

This leaf is graced with two colophons by Yün Shou-p'ing, written in 1680 on the occasion of his first, and last, visit to Wang Shih-min, who died soon after these were written:

> The mountaintops are black, sunlit but still wet;
> At the brushtip the spring clouds are dark and do not open.
> The ink-flowers drip, breaking the green mountains.
> Leaning on my desk, I suddenly hear the rain coming in the hills.

In early summer of the year *keng-shen* [1680], Nan-t'ien Shou-p'ing wrote this under the bamboo at Ho-lai-t'ang.

Mi father and son [Mi Fu, 1051-1107, and Mi Yu-jen, 1086-1165] and Kao Shang-shu [Kao K'o-kung] each went his separate way, as did Wang Hsi and Hsien [Wang Hsi-chih and Wang Hsien-chih], who rode together with Chung Yüan-ch'ang [Chung Yu]. Their ways have differences and yet are the same; they have similarities and yet are different.   Shou-p'ing.

Leaf G:

Landscape in the style of Mi Fu (1051-1107). Ink on paper. Height: 0.222 m.; width: 0.312 m.

Leaf HH:

Colophons by Li Tsung-k'ung (active second half of the seventeenth century), Ch'eng Sui (1605?-1691?) and Liu Yü (active in the K'ang-hsi reign, 1662-1722).

The colophon by Li Tsung-k'ung reads:

> Beyond the world of dust, the autumnal glow has a leisure of its own,
> Quiet man in a quiet scene, each is concerned only with the other.
> Who says that all along the road the scenery looks just like a painting?
> The painting is found between the red cliffs and the green trees.

Written on Shih-ku's [Wang Hui's] small painting for Master Yen-weng [Wang Shih-min].   Li Tsung-k'ung.

In the center is Ch'eng Sui's inscription:

> Opening this painting satisfies the wish to discover the beginning
>   [of the road].
> In clear dreams, I often roam with Creation;
> Without form, without limit, without end,
> Beyond the divine continent there are more divine continents.

Wu-mu-tzu [Wang Hui] painted for Master Yen-weng [Wang Shih-min] this small album which catches all of the principles and flavors of past and present. In the wielding of the axe it is supernatural and extraordinary. I have lived with it for ten days, and wrote this for [the Master's] correction.

Ch'eng Sui.

Finally, Liu Yü's colophon at the left:

> The grass and trees are covered with frost and dew,
> Red and yellow play one against the other.
> Below, the trees look down on the curve of a green stream,
> Above, they are on a level with the cold mountains.
> The woodcutter finds his way home,
> How randomly the wineshops are placed!
> Wisps of cloud cling to the rolling cliffs
> And a scarlet flag is propped at the corner of a building.
> In the morning one follows the brilliantly bright scenery,
> In the evening one is with the beauty of the misty glow.
> A rustling stream sweeps along the fallen leaves,
> A cool breeze sings on a high plateau.
> Leaning on a staff, I often pass such a scene,
> Chanting and singing make me only more melancholy.
> The world luxuriates in ornamental splendor,
> While heroes lose their youthful appearance.
> I believe, as a matter of course, that there is still a Tao,
> I urge you to think of [the ancient sages] Hsien-yüan
>   [the Yellow emperor] and Ch'i-pao.

Of Shih-ku-tzu's [Wang Hui's] paintings, I am especially fond of those in the school of Ni [Tsan], Huang [Kung-wang] and Ts'ao Chih-po. The fine and ornate [*kung-li*] ones, however, lean in an entirely different direction. If these too can be included in Yu-ch'eng's [Wang Wei's] Southern Tradition, what more can one ask?

Master Yen-weng [Wang Shih-min] searches for the *ta-ch'eng* [great synthesis] of painting. His opinions must be out of the ordinary!

Liu Yü of Pai-men.

Leaf H:

Landscape in the "blue-green" style. Ink and colors on paper. Height: 0.217 m.; width: 0.309 m.

124

On the mount to the right of the painting is a colophon by Chou Erh-yen (active in the K'ang-hsi reign, 1662-1722):

> The oak leaves are turning yellow, the maple leaves are red,
> Walking along, I seek for the right phrase; sitting down, I look at the scenery.
> Feeling thirsty, I purchase a strained, clear wine,
> But before I reach the mountains ahead, the exhilaration is gone.
>
> Chou Erh-yen of Chin-t'an inscribed for Master Yen-weng [Wang Shih-min].

To the left of the painting is a colophon by Yün Shou-p'ing:

> Dense forests and large boulders
> Act as hosts and guests.
> Beyond the hills, on a flat plain,
> A man returning travels the only road.

This composition gives the impression of great distance. The brushwork evokes the feeling of a T'ang master. I feel that [by comparison] even Wang Chin-ch'ing [Wang Shen, 1036?-after 1089] suffered from the ills of "carved painting" [*k'o-hua*]![18]   Shou-p'ing.

Leaf II: Blank.

Leaf I:

Landscape in the style of Kao K'o-kung (1248-1310). Ink on paper. Height: 0.223 m.; width: 0.335 m.

Beginning on the mount to the right of the painting and continuing on the left is a colophon by Yün Shou-p'ing:

> In the autumn of the year *jen-tzu* [1672], Shih-ku [Wang Hui] and I examined together a large scroll by Mi Nan-kung [Mi Fu] at Mr. Yang's "Water Pavilion." On it was an inscription by Sung Hui-miao [Emperor Hui-tsung, r. 1101-1126], which read: "Heaven bestows a timely rain, mountains and rivers appear through the clouds."
>
> Tung Tsung-po [Tung Ch'i-ch'ang, 1555-1636] authenticated it as "the finest painting by Mi." It was in the collection of Wu Kuang-lu of Ching-hsi

---

[18] *K'o-hua*—painting that is still and lifeless, due to too rigid an attention to technique and detail.

125

[I-hsing, Kiangsu]. Mr. Wu had a Yün-ch'i-lou [Tower of Rising Clouds] named after this painting. Shih-ku has used the same idea in creating this small picture. It is as if he had himself listened to the immortals' flute music at the Yüeh-yang-lou, and all mundane thoughts had suddenly vanished from his mind. Thus under his brush a supernatural breath rises like dense steam. The cloud-mountains which he has painted here are completely different from those before [i.e. on leaf G]. Yüan-k'o Shou-p'ing recorded this so that those who "understand the music" may appreciate the painting with him.

The year *kuei-ch'ou* [1673], summer, the sixteenth day of the sixth moon, under lamplight, while visiting Ching-hsi.

Leaf JJ:

Colophons by Yüan Yü-hsüan (active second half of the seventeenth century), and Ta Chung-kuang. The first reads:

> Green ridges, blue peaks, a hundred strange folds.
> The glow of the clear sky and the colors of the rain are matched in perfect harmony.
> For the man of leisure, there is endless relish,
> But it would be foolish to talk about this to a busy man of the world.

Inscribed on Wang-tzu Shih-ku's [Wang Hui's] painting after Kuo Ho-yang's [Kuo Hsi, active ca. 1020-1090] *Ch'ung-chiang kuei-tiao t'u* ["Sailing back along many rivers"] to beg for the correction of the old gentleman, Yen-weng [Wang Shih-min].   Yüan Yü-hsüan.

The colophon by Ta Chung-kuang is on the left:
> Weeping willows decorate a distant sand bank,
> A fishing boat idly drifts by the river's edge.
> No one is drunken and asleep at the cabin window,
> He must be at the wineshop, refilling his ewer.
> Inscribed for Master Yen-weng [Wang Shih-min] to raise a laugh.
>   Ta Chung-kuang.

Leaf J:

Landscape in the style of Kuo Hsi (active ca. 1020-1090). Ink on paper. Height: 0.224 m.; width: 0.325 m.

Leaf KK:

Colophon by Yeh Hsin (active second half of the seventeenth century):

> I once sailed on the Hsiang River in late summer and early autumn and saw the cloud patterns in the vast sky take many strange and unusual shapes. They looked very much like the snow-capped mountain forms of Kuo Ho-yang [Kuo Hsi]. Although all ancient painters were supposed to have heaven and earth as their teachers, Kuo Hsi was especially known for his cleverness [in painting nature's strange forms]. Now, seeing this album by Shih-ku [Wang Hui], I feel as if the strange clouds of the Hsiang River were once more vividly before my eyes. Who says that the ancients cannot be equaled by modern painters? I wrote this to query Master Yen-weng [Wang Shih-min]. Perhaps he will say that my words are not false.
>
> Yeh Jung-mu of Hsin-an writes this.

Leaf K:

Landscape in the style of Li Ch'eng (918-967) or Kuo Hsi (active ca. 1020-1090). Ink on paper. Height: 0.223 m.; width: 0.311 m.

On the mount to the right of the painting is a colophon by Li Tsung-k'ung (active second half of the seventeenth century):

> I gaze out at a range of mountains, pure and snowy white,
> And long for a letter, wondering how many bends there are in the river.
> The fisherman drifting towards me is in a happy mood,
> But I should know that he is not returning from Yen-ch'i.
>
> Li Tsung-k'ung inscribed.

Leaf LL:

Colophon by Ch'a Shih-piao (1615-1698):

> Even worms eating away at wood may happen to form patterns,
> Yet who can equal Ho-yang [Kuo Hsi], who made rocks like clouds?
> Do not say that all painters are clever,
> The best of them, past and present, will bow to you.
> All things successful have their special resources,
> With family teaching and a master's legacy, the accomplishments
>   will be doubly extraordinary.

Inheriting the mantle from Tung [Yüan] and Chü [-jan], the orthodox
  succession is yours,
 Your reputation will equal theirs for a thousand autumns.
 Inscribed on Shih-ku's [Wang Hui's] painting for Master Yen-weng's [Wang
Shih-min's] correction.   Ch'a Shih-piao.

Leaf L:

Landscape in the style of Kuo Hsi (active ca. 1020-1090). Ink on paper. Height: 0.226
m.; width: 0.335 m.

Wang Hui wrote the following inscription in the upper left corner of the painting:

> In the year *kuei-ch'ou* [1673], ninth moon, autumn, visiting at the Pi-yüan of
> Mr. Li of Wei-yang [Yangchow], I imitated a number of Sung and Yüan
> styles in small paintings, to be sent to my revered master, Yen-weng Feng-
> ch'ang [Wang Shih-min] to wish him a happy life, and also to take the place
> of waiting on him in person. His student, Wang Hui.

An inscription on the mounting to the right of the painting, by Yün Shou-p'ing, reads:

> Judging by this painting, Shih-ku [Wang Hui], has truly grasped the uncon-
> scious achievements of the ancient masters. In a land of tumbled mountains
> and wilderness, a single boat is adrift. How can such scenery be found in the
> bosom of an ordinary man?   Nan-t'ien Ts'ao-i [Yün Shou-p'ing].

To the left of the painting is an inscription by Chou Erh-yen (active in the K'ang-hsi
reign, 1662-1722):

> The river mist is thick and a fine drizzle whispers,
> The traveller is lonely, for with whom can he converse?
> In his small boat, carrying a crane, whither does he return?
> It must be to the Village of Yellow Leaves in Yü-shan [Wang Hui's
> native place].   [Chou Erh-]yen.

SEALS:

Wang Hui: *Shih-ku-tzu* (C & W, p. 67, no. 6), leaves A, B, D, J, K, and L; *Wang Shih-
ku* (three seals arranged vertically; C & W, p. 67, no. 18), leaves C and H; *Wang
Hui chih yin* (C & W, p. 67, no. 13) leaves F and G.

Wang Shih-min (1592-1680): *Wang Shih-min yin* (C & W, p. 49, no. 21), *Hsi-lu-lao-
jen* (C & W, p. 49, no. 25), both after his title.

Ch'a Shih-piao (1615-1698): *Erh-chan* (C & W, p. 213, no. 6) and *Shih-piao* (C & W, p.
213, no. 10), both on leaf LL.

Ch'eng Sui (ca. 1605-1691): *Ch'eng Sui* (C & W, p. 376, no. 3), leaf HH.

Ta Chung-kuang (1623-1692): *Chiang-shang wai-shih* (C & W, p. 312, no. 32), leaf AA; *Yang-lien* (C & W, p. 311, no. 19), leaf BB; *Ta Chung-kuang yin* (C & W, p. 311, no. 21), leaves BB and CC; *Yü-kang chü-shih*, leaf CC; *Chiang-shang wai-shih* (C & W, p. 311, no. 13), leaves E and JJ; *Chung-kuang* (C & W, p. 312, no. 30), leaf FF; *Chü-ch'ü shan-chuang*, leaf FF.

Yün Shou-p'ing (1633-1690): *Yün Shou-p'ing yin* (C & W, p. 357, no. 30), leaf B; *Cheng-shu* (C & W, p. 357, no. 2), leaf D; *Shou-p'ing* (C & W, p. 357, no. 14), leaves E and F; *Nan-t'ien hsiao-yin*, leaf F; *Shou-p'ing* (C & W, p. 357, no. 18), leaf GG; *Yün Cheng-shu* (C & W, p. 357, no. 25), leaf GG; *Nan-t'ien*, leaf GG; *Yüan-k'o* (C & W, p. 357, no. 22), leaves H and I; *Yün Shou-p'ing yin* (C & W, p. 357, no. 30), leaf I; *Shou-p'ing*, leaf L; *Shu-tzu*, leaf L.

Yüan Yü-hsüan (second half seventeenth century): *Yüan Yü-hsüan ssu-yin*, leaf JJ.

Hsiang-ts'ao-an chu-jen (second half seventeenth century): *Hsiang-ts'ao-an*, leaf A.

Li Tsung-k'ung (active second half seventeenth century): *Ch'in-lai*, leaf HH; *Li Tsung-k'ung yin*, leaf HH; *Shu Yün*, leaf HH; *Li Tsung-k'ung*, leaf K; *Ho shou*, leaf K.

Ch'en Ch'eng (active second half seventeenth century): *Tzu ai* and *Ch'en Ch'eng*, both leaf D.

Liu Yü (active ca. 1662-1722): *Liu Yü* (two seals arranged vertically), leaf C; *Liu Yü chih yin*, leaf HH; *Yü-ku*, leaf HH.

Hou Ch'üan (active ca. 1662-1772): *Ping-heng ch'ang-shou*, leaf F.

Chou Erh-yen (active ca. 1662-1722): *Erh-yen chih yin* (mourning seal in green), leaf H; *Chou Erh-yen yin* (mourning seal in green), leaf L.

Ta Chin-shan (unidentified): *Ta Chin-shan chia ts'ang yin*, leaf E.

Pi Lung (active c. 1736-1796): *Chu-ch'ih pi wan*, on second introductory double leaf; *Lou-tung Pi Lung Chien-fei-shih ts'ang* (C & W, p. 688, no. 28), on title leaf; *Pi Chien-fei pi-chi yin* (C & W, p. 688, no. 16), leaf L.

Chang Hsiung ? (1803-1886): *Chia-hsing Chang Chi-hsiung chen ts'ang yin*, on final leaf.

Shen Ping-ch'eng (1823-1895): *T'ieh-yen-lu chen-ts'ang*, on first opening inside cover, on title leaf, and on leaves A-L beside each painting.

Chu Ting-fu (unidentified): *Chu Ting-fu*, leaf D; *Ting-fu hsin-shang*, leaf H.

Wang Shih-hsin (unidentified, twentieth century): *Ch'ang-chou Wang Shih-hsin Yüeh-hsien chen ts'ang*, leaf L; *Wu-men Wang Yüeh-hsien chen ts'ang shu-hua p'u*, on final leaf.

Unidentified: *P'ing-shen yu shu-hua p'i*, leaf L.

Before entering the Morse Collection, the album was owned by Wang Shih-min (1592-1680), Ta Chin-shan (unidentified), Pi Lung (a noted collector active in the Ch'ien-lung reign, 1736-1796), Shen Ping-ch'eng (1823-1895), Chang Chi-hsiung (? Chang Hsiung, 1803-1886), Wang Yüeh-hsien (or Wang Shih-hsin, twentieth century ?). The album was probably mounted in its present form while in the collection of Shen Ping-ch'eng, who affixed his seal beside each of the paintings. At that time, Pi Lung's cartouche was removed from the original cover and placed on the second blank leaf.

The album was displayed in the Venice exhibition of Chinese Art in 1954, honoring the 700th anniversary of the birth of Marco Polo. Two leaves, E and I, are reproduced in the catalogue, *Arte Cinese* (Venice, 1954), p. 241. It was then owned by M. Jean Pierre Dubosc.

16a. *Ch'ü Ku*
(In Pursuit of Antiquity)

太上

神

時敏

吉

懶學楊雄作解
嘲愛香時玩易
中文約庄不到
眠愛唯有青山
似舊戈為
煙舫先生書政
董其昌

16AA

16A

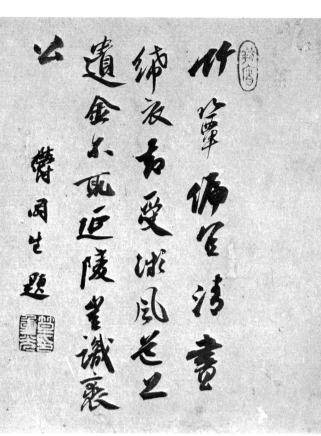

竹窗偏室清畫
絺衣古受逃風老之
遺金不瓦延陵尝識裹
公

磬同生題

16 BB

偶一展對勿忽置身荒崖邃谷舜冥無人之境樹影森森蕭砌
路盤紆景不盡天游賞無窮自非疑神獨照誂落靈氣
妙筆先生機直寄於之趣若未易臻此　石谷子為
煙翁先生挑北苑小景真麂化神明第一合作壽平題

16 B

天青雲白樹蒼〻
茅屋疏籬野岫
衡重〻牧童生皆稚
芒𡶶橫笛引斜陽
書於
烟翁先生博𥥊　重寀

16 CC

楊柳和金綠蘺〻滿水邨
東風陣〻主拂不頻𥥊長門
越峯

16 C

癡翁畫法正經位置皆可學而至惟筆
墨之外別有一種荒率蒼莽之氣則不可學
而至故學癡翁者不待真能臻斯境者
婁東奉常先生與虞山石谷子耳
　　　　　　　　　壽平敬志

為憐筆墨有同心心理相思暇即
尋深夜篝燈看作畫不知何處發
　清音
　　題烏目山人倣巨然小景畫陵題

16D

石谷子倣雲西竹石粘接靈趣蕭瑟索玩芳畫昔人所謂
一勺水亦有曲處一片石亦有深廔此畫得之矣惲壽平題

16E

兩頰春筍滿林霏更有櫻桃
顆〻圓佗渭山中風味好教人羨
向五庚延
書代
姻愚老先生政之　重光

作畫須有解衣盤礴傍若無人意然後化機在手元氣狼
藉不為先匠所拘兩游度之外矣　壽平題
觀寫目王叔村明本真足辟易群深乃洞心駭目之賞也次日又題

16G

峯頭黛色晴猶濕華
底春雲暗不開墨華
淋漓翠潑斷隱几凬闐
山雨來
　庚申初夏南田壽平題于鶴來
堂竹下

米家父子專高尚書今路揚鑣之猶
王民義載砒与鍾元常並驅於其門徑
肴異而同者同可異者　壽平

16 GG

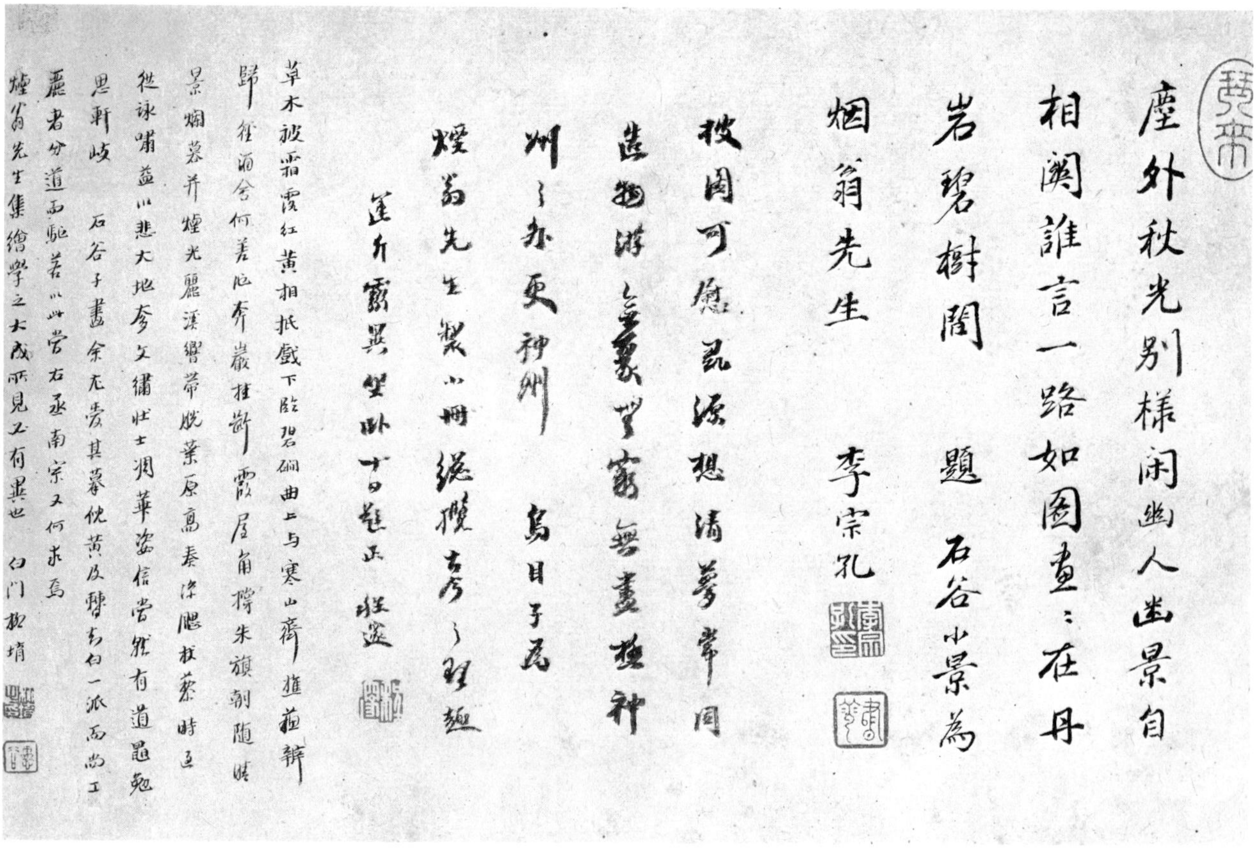

塵外秋光別樣閑幽人幽景自

相関誰言一路如圖畫:在丹

岩碧樹間　題　石谷小景為

烟翁先生　李宗孔

披圖可憶亂源想清夢常関

造物游意意蒙世窮無畫極神

州之外更神州　烏目子尾

烟翁先生製此冊緣擥古之佳趣

崔升霸異望卧竹日慈正　継盗

草木披霜霞紅黃相抵戲下臨碧嗣曲上与寒山齋推菴辭

歸徑酒含何�≈應喬巖挂斷霞屋角檐朱旆剝随晚

景煙暮并煙光麗溪響帶烘葉原高春深盤華峯時豆

従詠嘯益川悲大地參文繡壯士潤華盗当然有道題勉

思軔岐石谷子畫余無爱其蓁怳黃及聲喜白一派高出工

麗者分道而驅若此尝石丞南宗又何求為

煙翁先生集繪學之大成乃見古有恭世

白門楸埴

槲葉初黃楓葉丹行来覺自生素肩渴時買浮

源清酒欲玉前山興巴闌

　　　　金壇周而衍題呈

煙翁先生

密林大石相為主賓山公平原歸人一徑位置極盡觀覧

運筆有唐賢之風覧王晉卿猶傷刻畫

　　　　壽平

壬子秋興石谷在揚氏水亭同觀來南宮大幀宗微廟題云天降時兩山川
出雲董宗伯鑒定來真第一為荊溪吳光祿所藏吳氏青雲起樓畫蓋以斯南名
其石谷用其意為小幀如逸兵陽樓觀聽仙人吹笛一時兒境頃盡拔下筆靈

氣蓊鬱達興前此所圖雲山象景園客奇平題与賞音者共鑒之
癸丑夏六月望後一旦燈下在荊溪寓中

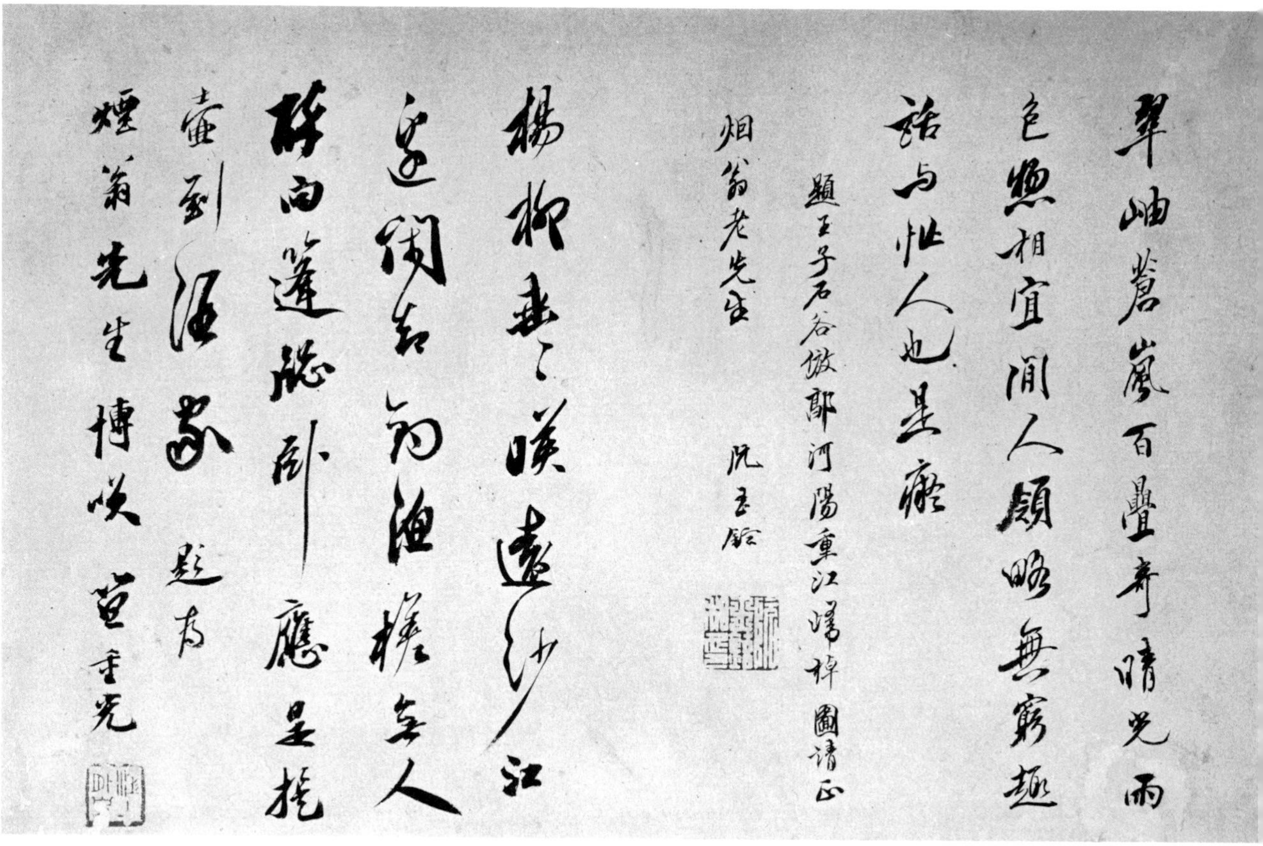

翠岫蒼巖百疊奇晴光雨
色總相宜閒人頗略無窮趣
話與怡人也甚麁

烟翁老先生

擬王子石谷倣郎河陽重江疊嶂圖請正

阮元銘

楊柳垂垂映遠沙江
遠銜名句漁樵在人
醉向蓬窗臥應是把
壺到漁家
煙菊先生博咲草聖兄
題為

16 JJ

16 J

16KK

今歲夏秋之間沉舟湘上見
去冬雪所怪之奇之大似郭
河陽雪山古人雖曰天地爲
師而師匠尤稱巧手今見石
谷蒞冊覽得上奇雲氣其云
目然謂非今人所及邪
書以質之
煙客先生戒渭尒谨示课
新安葉榮甫題

儗三望裏一堆山野破瓊瑤水繞灣泛之漁
人高興在須知不是剡溪還　李宗孔題

16K

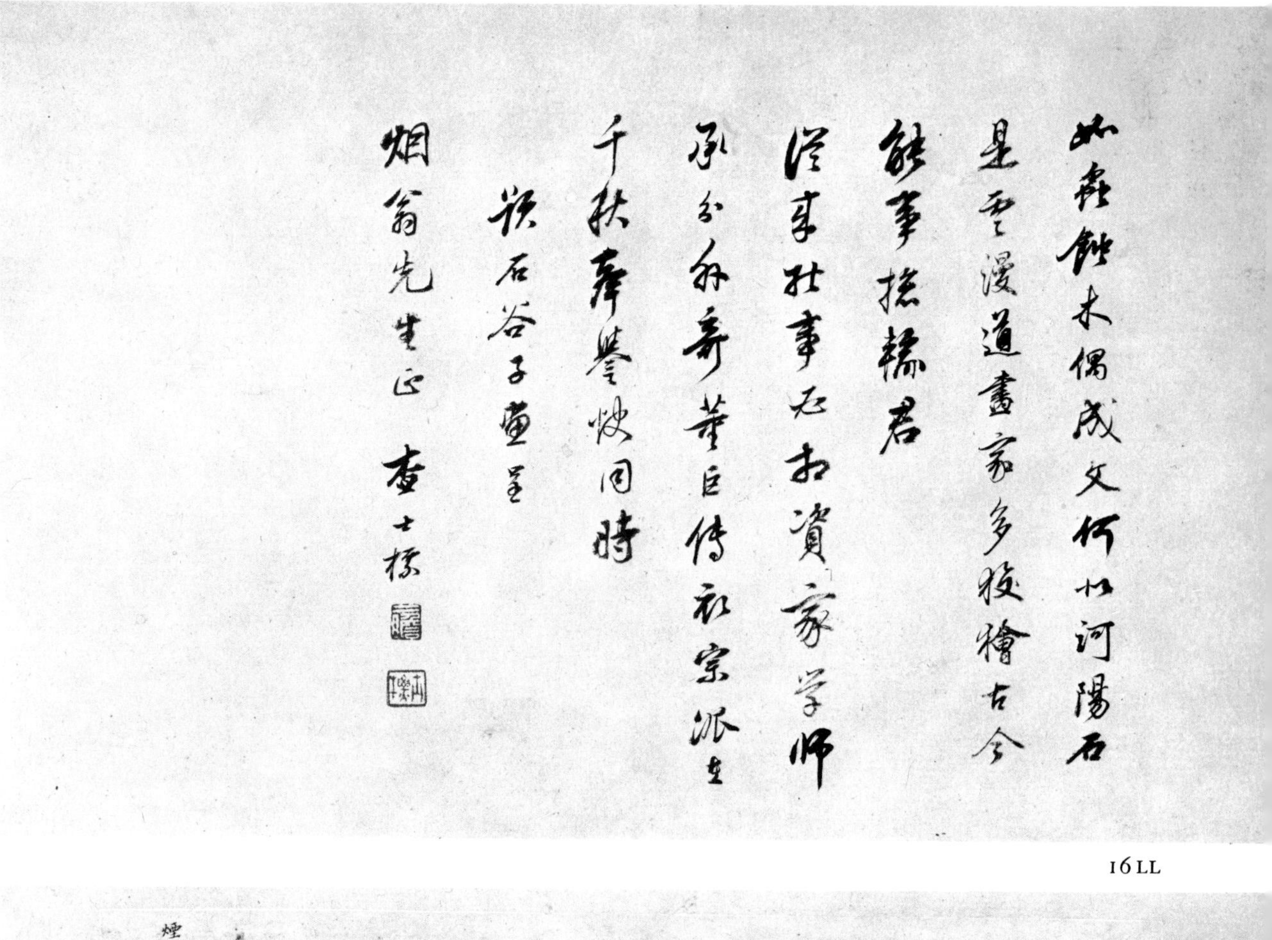

如畫缺木偶成文何如河陽石
是云澹道畫家多披繪古今
能事推穩君
澤季杜事石坞資家學師
承名孙奇葉臣傳私宗派生
千秋声誉炊同時
頑石谷子董星
煙翁先生正　李士樟

癸丑九秋暑雜揚李氏之祖園
雜依宗元小品寄呈
煙翁朱常尊先生景序和以
當覬對
後學王肇

漠漠溪煙細雨喧宏情孤迴與誰論扁舟
載鶴歸何處只在雲山黃葉村

豐石石四本真玩李古人不用心慶笑
亂山蒼遠一棟渺此凡俗宵中有此
境界不　南昌草衣

17 Landscape in the style of Wu Chen (1280-1354).

> Dated 1675. Hanging scroll, ink on paper. Height: 0.672 m.; width: 0.393 m.

Wang Hui's inscription, top center, reads:

> The year *i-mao* [1675], late spring, imitating Mei-hua-an-chu's [Wu Chen's] *Hsia Shan t'u* ["Summer Mountains"]; I ask the criticism of Master Luan-sheng.   Wu-mu-shan-chung-ch'iao-che, Wang Hui.

To the right of Wang Hui's inscription is a colophon by Wang Chien (1598-1677):

> Tung Wen-min [Tung Ch'i-ch'ang, 1555-1636] often said to me: "Painters who possess the qualities of beauty and elegance [*wen-hsiu chih chih*] may yet lack roundness and fullness [*hun-hou*]; and those who have power and strength [*ch'iu-ching chih li*] may yet be partly lacking in style and resonance [*feng-yün*]." As for Shih-ku [Wang Hui], all of the desirable qualities seem to be present. It may be said that not a single hair in his painting is to be regretted. This painting is deep and calm and quietly aloof. The *yüan-ch'i* [primal breath] seems to flow magically through it. It is one of the great masterpieces, and should be carefully treasured.
>   Wang Chien of Lou-shui inscribed.

SEALS:

Wang Hui: *Tzu-yi-yüeh*, before his inscription; *Shih-ku-tzu* (C & W, p. 67, no. 6) and *Wang Hui chih yin* (C & W, p. 67, no. 19), after his inscription; *Lai-ch'ing-ko* (C & W, p. 68, no. 66), lower right corner.

Wang Chien (1598-1677): *Lai-yün-kuan*, before his colophon; *Wang Chien chih yin* (C & W, p. 82, no. 10), after his colophon; *Hsiang-pi* (C & W, p. 82, no. 12), after his colophon.

There are no collectors' seals on the painting, and no record has been found, though Hsü Pang-ta has listed it as a painting that he had seen and confirmed (*Li-tai liu-ch'uan shu-hua tso-p'in pien-nien-piao*, Shanghai, 1963, referring to his own record in *Ku-tai shu-hua kuo-mu hui-k'ao fu-mu*). The present mounting may well be the original of the seventeenth century.

蓋文敦常與予論丹青家具文秀之質
而渾厚未之得道勁之力而風韻不全全
如君谷眾美畢具可謂毫髮無遺憾
矣此圖澹沱遠元章靈通九楊髁心
良可寶也　姜水王鑑題

乙卯暮春倣梅花庵主夏山圖並立
鶴芹先生
烏目山中樵者王翬

No. 17

17 a. Detail,
actual size

No. 18

WANG HUI

18   River Island on a Clear Autumn Day.
Chiang-chu ch'iu-ch'ing.

> Dated 1680. Fan, ink and colors on paper. Height: 0.179 m.; width: 0.55 m.
Inscription:

River Islands on a Clear Autumn Day

> The year *keng-shen* [1680], the intercalary month, the 28th day, written for
my colleague Yü, old brother.   Wang Hui.

SEALS:

Wang Hui: *Wang Hui* (C & W, p. 67; no. 17).
Miss Alice Boney, Tokyo: *P'ang Nai.   so-ts'ang.*
Unidentified: *Ching-su-shih so-ts'ang.*

19   Mountain Hermitage on a Clearing Autumn Day, in the style of Wang Meng (1308-1385).

> Collection of The Art Museum, Princeton University (66-97). Gift of Mr. and Mrs. Earl Morse.

Shan-chuang ch'iu-chi t'u.

> Dated 1692. Handscroll; ink and colors on paper. Height: 0.307 m.; length: 3.987 m.

At the end of the scroll is an inscription by Wang Hui:

> The year being *jen-shen* [1692], spring, first month, sixteenth day, imitating Huang-ho shan-jen's [Wang Meng's] "Mountain Hermitage on a Clearing Autumn Day."   Shih-ku, Wang Hui.

Attached to the end of the scroll is a colophon by the nineteenth-century painter, calligrapher and collector, Lo T'ien-ch'ih (*chin-shih* in 1826):

> To the right is Keng-yen-san-jen's [Wang Hui's] imitation of Shu-ming's [Wang Meng's] "Mountain Hermitage on a Clearing Autumn Day." [It is of the] divine class, topmost level [*shen-p'in shang-shang*]. Tao-kuang, fifteenth year, *i-wei* [1835], on the day of the festival of Washing the Buddha [eighth day of the fourth month], I obtained it in Liang-i Studio, Liu-li ch'ang, in the capital [Peking]. Lo T'ien-ch'ih of Ling-nan authenticated. Inscribed at Ju-ju-chiao-hsiu-kuan.

SEALS:

Wang Hui: *Shih-ku-tzu* (C & W, p. 67, no. 6), after his inscription; *Wang Hui chih yin* (C & W, p. 67, no. 19), after his inscription.

Hua Kuei (active ca. 1662-1735): *Kuang-han kung ch'ung-kuang*, lower right at beginning.

Lo T'ien-ch'ih (received *chin-shih* degree in 1826): *Lo-shih Liu-hu*, after his colophon.

P'an Chien-an (active ca. 1851-1861): *P'an Yen-ling yin* (C & W, p. 621, no. 1), lower right at beginning; *Ts'eng ts'ang P'an Chien-an ch'u* (C & W, p. 621, no. 3), lower left at end.

P'an Shih-ch'eng (*chin-shih* in 1832): *P'an Te-yü shen-ting*, lower right at beginning; *P'an Shih-ch'eng yin*, lower left at end; *Te-yü hsin-shang*, lower left at end.

Before entering the Morse Collection, the scroll was owned by Hua Ch'uan (or Hua Kuei, active ca. 1662-1735), Lo T'ien-ch'ih (*chin-shih* in 1826), P'an Chien-an (active ca. 1851-1861) and P'an Shih-ch'eng (*chin-shih* in 1832). It is recorded in Kuan Mien-chün (twentieth century), *San-ch'iu-ko shu hua lu*, ch. *hsia*, p. 13 a/b.

19a. Detail,
actual size

WANG HUI

20   Winter Landscape.

    Undated. Hanging scroll; ink and colors on silk. Height: 1.73 m.; width: 0.718 m.

In the top right corner Wang Hui has inscribed a couplet:

> In every place the winter snows collect on the buildings;
> In every house a spring wind is made drunk by pipes and strings.

In the lower right corner he has added his signature and seal:

> Wang Hui respectfully painted.

No. 20

WANG HUI

21   Landscape in the style of Ni Tsan.

Dated 1710. Hanging scroll; ink on paper. Height: 1.028 m.; width: 0.563 m.

Preceding his own inscription, Wang Hui first copied the following inscriptions by Ni Tsan from the original painting:

The year *wu-shen* [1368], sixth month, first day, convalescing in a quiet studio [I] inscribed:

Mist from the banks gradually covers the waves of the lake.
In the sixth month, the chill lightened the green color of moths.
I only love the big plantain leaves before the window,
Their greenery spread out, a tall fan receiving the plenteous wind.
Today a damp chill attacked me.
Fifth day, again inscribed:
Little by little the green moss [seems] about to grow over my clothes;
Across a pond of spring water young cranes fly.
To the deserted village, silent and empty, few people come;
There is only the studio-boat beside the bamboo gate.
Evening of the seventh day, idly written on an empty part of the paper.

[Ni] Tsan.

Lord Chang of Crane Studio is complete in the Five Blessings [longevity, wealth, health, virtue, completing one's allotted span of life]. Wen-po of Hua-t'ing is a learned antiquarian, fond of elegance, it is said.   [Ni] Tsan.

After these, Wang Hui also transcribed the following by Shao Kuan (unidentified):

Ten years in wind and snow I travelled in Nan-chou [Szechwan],
With alarm I see the streams and mountains, to my eyes doubly gloomy.
What land could possibly be like that in the painting?
In green grass-raincloak, in mist and rain, he moors his fishing-boat.

Shao Kuan.

Wang Hui's own inscription reads:

Whenever I see a genuine work by Ni Tsan, it is usually a small composition showing a *p'ing-yüan* ["flat distance"]. This scroll has many peaks stacked up like layers of stone screens: it is completely derived from Ching [Ching Hao, late ninth century], and Kuan [Kuan T'ung, active ca. 907-923], and is a work that has never been seen before. I saw the scroll at Mr. Chang's [Chang

Hsiu-yü's] house in Jun-chou. Now having imitated it from memory, I suddenly seem to have been placed amidst Mount K'uang-lu and the peaks of Heng. The year *keng-yin* [1710], spring, the first month, the fifteenth day.

Wu-mu-shan-chung-jen, Wang Hui.

SEALS:

Wang Hui: *T'ai-yüan* (C & W, p. 68, no. 51), before his own inscription; *Wang Hui chih yin* (C & W, p. 68, no. 39) and *Keng-yen-san-jen shih nien ch'i-shih-yu-chiu* (C & W, p. 68, no. 70), both after his inscription; *Ch'ü ch'iao ya ch'ü* (C & W, p. 69, no. 81) and *Ch'ing-hui lao-jen*, both in the lower right corner.

Li Shan-lan (1810-1882): *Tse-hu-hsi-chai*, lower left corner.

Hu Hsiao-cho (late nineteenth century): *Hu Hsiao-cho ts'ang*, lower left; *Huai-yin Hu shih chia ts'ang*, lowest left on mounting.

Weng Pin-sun (late nineteenth century): *Weng Pin-sun yin*, lower left on mounting.

Chang Ta-ch'ien (born 1899): *Ta-feng-t'ang chen ts'ang yin*, lower right; *Nan-pei-tung-hsi chih yü hsiang-sui wu pieh-li*, lower right.

Wang Chi-ch'ien (C. C. Wang, born 1907): *Wang Chi-ch'ien hai-wai so-chien ming chi*.

A painting attributed to Ni Tsan, with all the colophons that Wang Hui transcribed, was formerly in the collection of P'ang Yüan-chi (reproduced as *Tseng Chou Po-ang Ch'i-shan-t'u* in *T'ang Sung Yüan Ming Ch'ing hua-hsüan*, Shanghai, 1960, pl. 26). Its composition, however, bears no similarity to the Morse painting.

A somewhat different version of the second of the two Ni Tsan poems copied onto this painting by Wang Hui is found in Ni Tsan's collected poems (*Ni Yün-lin Hsien-sheng shih-chi*, Ssu-pu-ts'ung-k'an ed., chüan 6, p. 12b), and has been translated by Arthur Waley (*An Introduction to the Study of Chinese Painting*, p. 243). Wang Hui also re-copied the same two poems onto a small album leaf painted in 1712.

Before entering the Morse Collection, the painting was owned by Li Shan-lan, Hu Hsiao-cho, Weng Pin-sun, Chang Ta-ch'ien, and C. C. Wang. It is recorded in Li Tso-hsien (1807-1876), *Shu-hua Chien-ying* (1871), chüan 23, pp. 13a/b. Li, who seems to have consistently recorded all seals on the paintings he included, here records only those of Wang Hui. Apparently, therefore, Li Shan-lan, Hu Hsiao-cho and Weng Pin-sun owned the painting in the later part of the nineteenth century.

戊申六月一日養疴靜軒題汀烔舟霞湖
波六月寒生淺翠蛾獨愛窗前蕉葉綠
羅高扇受風多是日陰寒襯人
五日又題點青苔欲上衣一池春水鵁雛飛荒
村開窘人稀到只有書舟傍竹扉
者云增　　　七夕日謬寫紙空增
鶡齋張公於五福齋文伯華事之博古好雅
十年風雪走南州愁見
溪流眼恰出烱何地可能知畫
裏綠萎烟雨縈溪舟
邛賈

崇
為兄雲林先生仿以半
志天惕者居為此情
重崙疊峰金徽荊
關其屬示者之作余
漢泗州張氏借觀迷
著之一匡忧置我于匡
鹰衙獄問關
庚寅春正月望日
為旦山中人王翬

No. 21

21 a. Detail
actual size

22   The Wisteria Studio, in the style of Wang Meng.
T'eng-hua shu-wu.

Dated 1712. Hanging scroll; ink and slight color on paper. Height: 1.182 m.; width: 0.594 m.

Wang Hui's inscription, in the upper right corner, reads:

The Wisteria Studio.

K'ang-hsi [reign, the year] *jen-chen* [1712], mid-autumn, imitating Huang-ho-shan-ch'iao's [Wang Meng's] brush.   Shih-ku-tzu, Wang Hui.

Mounted above the painting is a title inscription written by the nineteenth-century calligrapher and painter, Pao Chün (*chin-shih* in 1823):

Keng-yen-san-jen's [Wang Hui's] Wisteria Studio, imitating the ancients.
Shih-ch'i-sheng, Pao Chün inscribed.

A colophon written by Pao Chün is attached below the painting. It reads:

I myself painted streams and mountains and the retired scholar's home,
Blue pines, green bamboo, purple wisteria blossoms.
All poets, ancient and modern, respond to the same mood.
You, sir, are "cultivating the mist" (*keng-yen*, i.e. Wang Hui), and I, "lean upon radiant clouds."
I newly built a small pavilion at Yung-t'ang, and the Ssu-ma Chang Nan-shan wrote the inscription [on it], calling it "Leaning upon Radiant Clouds."
Tao-kuang [reign, the year] *keng-wu* [1850], in the winter months, at an inn in Su-men, idly inscribed. I-ch'ing [Pao Chün].

SEALS:

Wang Hui: *Hsi-shuang* (C & W, p. 68, no. 55), before his inscription; *Keng-yen* (C & W, p. 68, no. 53) and *Ch'ing-hui-lao-jen shih-nien pa-shih-yu-i* (C & W, p. 68, no. 80), after his inscription; *Ch'ü ch'iao ya ch'ü* (C & W, p. 68, no. 81), *Pu erh fa* (C & W, p. 68, no. 64), and *Wo ssu ku-jen* (C & W, p. 68, no. 65), at lower right.
Pao Chün (*chin-shih* in 1823): *Kung-tse shou*, before his inscription; *Pao-chün ssu yin* and *Shen-hsien-chüan-shu*, after his inscription; *Feng-shan* and *Pao-chün chih yin*, after his colophon.
Ma Chi-tsu (Contemporary Hong Kong dealer): *Ma Chi-tsu yin*, at lower right.
Unidentified: *Yün-ch'ao hsin-shang*, at lower right.

The painting was presented to Wang Hui's friend, Hou Ch'üan, by the painter upon its completion (according to *Ch'ing-hui tseng-yen, chüan* 2, p. 9a). Subsequent owners include the nineteenth-century calligrapher and painter, Pao Chün, and, most recently, Miss Alice Boney.

No. 22

WANG HUI

23   Landscape in the styles of Chü-jan (act. ca. 960-980) and Yen Wen-kuei (967-1044).

    Dated 1713. Handscroll; ink and colors on paper. Height: 0.309 m.; length: 4.013 m.

Wang Hui's inscription, at the end of the scroll, reads:

> Some years ago I was a guest in the capital [Peking], where, at the home of a collector, I was able to see a great many scrolls by ancient men. Among them were two paintings: Chü-jan's *Chiang-kuan hsiao-chi* ["River Pass on a Clearing Morning"], and Yen Wen-Kuei's *Shan-k'ou pu-yü* ["Fishing near a Mountain Pass"]. Their "divine color" (*shen-ts'ai*) was magnificent, and each was extremely refined and marvelous, at the head of all of the famous works of Sung and Yüan. Suddenly, after more than twenty years, they have come to my breast. This scroll was made by combining the two masters' general concepts. Although in purity, truth, and subtle blandness it is not necessarily extremely similar, yet neither is its style very far from them.
>
> The year *kuei-ssu* [1713], three days after the Ch'ung-yang festival [ninth day of the ninth month].
>
> Wu-mu-shan-chung-jen, Wang Hui recorded.

SEALS:

Wang Hui: *T'ai-yüan* (C & W, p. 68, no. 51), before his inscription; *Wang Hui chih yin* (C & W, p. 68, no. 39), after his inscription; *Keng-yen* (C & W, p. 68, no. 53), *Ch'ing-hui-lao-jen shih nien pa-shih-yu-erh* (C & W, p. 68, no. 79), in lower left corner; *Fu-ch'un kao chi, Lai-ch'ing-ko* (C & W, p. 68, no. 66) and *Wo ssu ku-jen* (C & W, p. 68, no. 65), in lower right corner.

Wang Chi-ch'ien (C. C. Wang, born 1907): *Chi-ch'ien hsin-shang,* lower right; *Wang Chi-ch'ien hai-wai so-chien ming-chi,* lower left, on mounting.

Unidentified: *Yu-shih chen ts'ang,* lower right; *Chen-ting Wang-shih,* upper left.

23a. Detail,
actual size

WANG HUI

Forgery of Huang Kung-wang (1209-1354).

24   Landscape.

       Hanging scroll; ink on paper. Height: 0.604 m.; width: 0.295 m.

Inscription:

       The reign of Yüan-t'ung, first year [1333], second month, painted at Chih-
chih-t'ang.   Ch'ih-weng [Huang Kung-wang].

SEALS:

Forged Huang Kung-wang: *Ta-ch'ih*, with inscription.
Unidentified: *Shih-ni ts'eng-shang*, lower left; *Ku-? Wang-shih*, lower right.

No. 24

25a. Detail

Modern forgery after Wang Hui

25   Landscape.

    Dated 1686. Hanging scroll; ink and colors on paper. Height: 1.363 m.; width: 0.467 m.

Inscription:

    For long I have felt the tip of my brush to be slow;
    I write painting just as one writes *li* style calligraphy.
    Except for the single sound of the yellow crane, the mountain hut is quiet.
    The man of *tao* has just woken from his afternoon sleep.
    The year ping-yin [1686], spring.   Wang Hui of Ku-yü.

SEALS:

Forged Wang Hui: *Wang Hui chih yin, Keng-yen.*

Yao Ta-jung (unidentified): *P'u-ting Yao Ta-jung tzu Li-huan hao Chih-feng chin-shih-shu-hua.*

No. 25

YÜN SHOU-P'ING (1633-1690)

26   Landscape.

Undated. Hanging scroll; ink and colors on silk. Height: 1.335 m.; width: 0.638 m.

Inscription:

> Men's houses keep to the shallow streams;
> Mists cover the root of the mountain.
> Where should I let my ink flowers fall?
> Like the mist-petals, I would leave no trace.

Some characters are missing in the remainder of the inscription:

... [vertical and] horizontal *ts'un* strokes mix together without careful thought. [This is something that] cannot be put in words, nor can it be learnt. It is like the poem by T'ai-po [Li Po, 701-762], [which says:] "The falling leaves collect and again scatter; The young crows roost and are frightened away again." [19] Vaguely one can [obtain] a resemblance to this.

[Shou-p'ing] wrote at the T'iao-hua-chai.

SEALS:

Yün Shou-p'ing: *Shou-p'ing* and *Yün Cheng-shu*.
Unidentified: *Ho-chou; Wang-shih chien-shang chih chang*.

[19] *Ssu-pu pei-yao, Li T'ai-po ch'üan chi*, ch. 25, 10b.

166

人家依棷瀨嵐氣照山根
墨畫何蒙荗岠軍嶺
委嗳

陶絨源相主
寄寄汰不禊凜如太
如棄熊遙散雾㽞
一寿其棄
賀于菶平齋

No. 26

WANG YÜAN-CH'I (1642-1715)

27   Landscape in the style of Huang Kung-wang and Kao K'o-kung.

Dated 1705. Hanging scroll; ink on paper; height: 1.146 m.; width: 0.542 m.

Inscription:

Although Ta-ch'ih [Huang Kung-wang] and Fang-shan [Kao K'o-kung] are separate, they both are descended from Tung Yüan and Chü-jan; one could speak of them being in the same family. When Tung Tsung-po [Tung Ch'i-ch'ang] painted he often combined their ideas. This painting imitates him, but being done hurriedly, is unable to obtain his breath-resonance. The time being the year *i-yu* of the K'ang-hsi period [1705], inscribed on a spring day while traveling by boat on the Yü-feng-tao.   Wang Yüan-chi.

Superscription:

Once I had a small painting by Ni Kao-shih [Ni Tsan]. The Ssu-nung Lu t'ai [Wang Yüan-ch'i] saw it and liked it. He considered that it had both bone and spirit, and that its meaning was beyond words. He enjoyed it so much that I was most embarrassed. Now at Yü-shu-chai I have seen a painting by the Ssu-nung imitating the Six Gentlemen in which he successfully used the brush ideas of Tung [Yüan] and Chü[-jan]. The difference between this and my former work is no less than that between heaven and earth. I am ashamed, I am ashamed. The year *i-yu*, in mid-winter, Ho I recorded.

SEALS:

Wang Yüan-ch'i: *Yü Shu Hua-t'u liu yü jen k'an* (C & W, p. 42, no. 59), before inscription; *Wang Yüan-ch'i yin* (C & W, p. 41, no. 26), after inscription; *Lu-t'ai* (C & W, p. 41, no. 40), after inscription; *Hsi-lu-hou-jen* (C & W, p. 42, no. 63), lower left.

Ho I (ca. 1700): *Ho I* and *Tan-shih*, after his colophon.

Weng T'ung-ho (1830-1904): *Yü-shan Weng T'ung-ho yin* and *Shu-p'ing hua-chien*, lower left, on mounting.

Chang Ta-ch'ien (born 1899): *Ta-feng-t'ang chen-ts'ang yin*, lower left corner of colophon; *Nan-pei-tung-hsi chih yu hsiang-sui wu pieh-li* and *Ni-yen-lou*, lower right.

Wang Chi-ch'ien (C. C. Wang, born 1907): *Chi-ch'ien hsin-shang*, lower right.

168

大痴房山门庭雅别嫡宗
董巨而循一家春属世董宗
伯作畫本意用其气以自固然
之妙之行後中呈雅翁具氣
韻此者
康熙乙圖春日题扵玉峯道
中舟次
王原祁

No. 27

YANG CHIN (1644-1728)

28   Landscape with figures.

Dated 1726. Hanging scroll; ink and colors on paper. Height: 1.195 m.; width: 0.543 m.

Inscription:

The village boys are used to herding the water-buffaloes;
Securely riding on their backs they attend the land of immortals.
With only a straw raincoat they don't turn back for mist or rain.
The red polygonum and the white frogbit show each other off,
The water birds and the land birds together bob up and down.
I have striven to express this in a painting.

The year *ping-wu*, autumn, the seventh month, the 16th day.

Eighty-three-year-old Hsi-t'ing, Yang Chin wrote.

SEALS:

Yang Chin: *Chia-shen* (the cyclical date for 1644, the year of Yang Chin's birth), before inscription; *Yang Chin* (C & W, p. 408, no. 3) and *Tzu-ho*, after inscription; *T'ien-chen lan-man shih wu shih* and *Hsi-t'ing Ho-tao-jen* (C & W, p. 705, no. 52), lower right.

Chang Jo-ai (1713-1746): *Ch'ing-ho Chang Jo-ai Ch'ing-lan shih chen-wan chih chang* (C & W, p. 678, no. 22) and *Tzu-tzu-sun-sun yung-pao-yung*, lower left.

Unidentified: *Tz'u-chien chen-shang*, lower left.

170

趙令穰每一落筆靜秀
之光樸人顏面而論者
猶以不讀書少之夫讀
書何如以道于畫池武告
我曰能讀書人于天地化
工之氣山川性情之愛無
所不見行百今峰山厯落
之事僉與花月之竟天
寒歲暮之慈倦有所放
感排官而出而出名不知即
然則讀書三字堂徒一畫理
耶环山方士鳥年識

No. 29

FANG SHIH-SHU (1692-1751)

29   Landscape.

Undated. Hanging scroll; ink and colors on paper. Height: 0.681 m.; width: 0.462 m.

Inscription:

Whenever Chao Ling-jang [act. ca. 1070-1100] painted, his clear and elegant brightness struck people intimately. Those who discussed this belittled it by saying that it was because he did not read books. What is this reading of books? Someone who took it to be the same as painting told me: "For the man who reads books, of the creation of heaven and earth, of the love of feelings for mountains and streams, there is nothing that he does not perceive. In ancient and modern times, in difficult and disordered affairs, in the joy of birds, flowers or the moon, in the sadness of winter or the end of the year, in all these he can express his pleasure or grief, though in doing so he may not be aware of it." But as for the two words "reading books," how can you explain them just through one theory of painting?

Fang Shih-shu of Huan-shan [painted] and inscribed.

SEALS:

Fang Shih-shu: *Fang Shih-shu yin* (C & W, p. 24, no. 6); *Huan-shan* (C & W, p. 24, no. 3); *Hsün-yüan mo-ku.*
Unidentified: *Chung-t'ao chen-shang.*

173

Wang Hui, Wang Yüan-ch'i and Wu Li

An Addendum by Wen Fong

AFTER Roderick Whitfield's catalogue had been completed, Mr. and Mrs. Earl Morse added three more paintings to their collection. Wang Yüan-ch'i's "Wang-ch'uan Villa" of 1711 (No. 31) and Wu Li's "Passing the Summer at the Thatched Hall of Inkwell" of 1679 (No. 32) were acquired from the collection of Mr. C. C. Wang. Wang Hui's hanging scroll "Snow Clearing" dated 1669 (No. 30) was presented to Mr. and Mrs. Morse by Mr. Wang. Since Dr. Whitfield now lives in London, I have the privilege of introducing these newly acquired paintings.   W. F.

I

THE orthodox school of landscape painting, as exemplified by these three painters, represented the major thrust of the artistic rejuvenation that occurred in the early Ch'ing dynasty. The late Ming, much like our own time, was a period of bitter social disengagement and intellectual dissent. In the field of painting, the dwindling leadership of the Wu and Che Schools had opened the way to a host of independent painters who experimented with and searched for new forms. Out of this period of diversity and conflict a new orthodoxy emerged. Tung Ch'i-ch'ang and his followers defined the so-called Southern School tradition in the history of painting as the orthodox, correct approach, "the lamp that shines forever," against all aberrant ways. By reaffirming certain ancient values, Tung and his followers achieved a renewal of life and meaning in art through traditional means.

In turning painting into an abstract art comparable to calligraphy, by insisting that "if we talk about the wonders of brush and ink, then [nature's] landscape can never equal painting," Tung accomplished the extraordinary feat of shifting the art of painting onto entirely new technical and critical grounds.[20] He established a set of rules and creative possibilities which were to influence and govern the so-called "Individualist" painters no less than the orthodox masters of the early Ch'ing. While the paintings of the individualists Tao-chi and Chu Ta represented the release of individual genius through Tung's teachings on an intuitive plane, it was in the works of the mature generation of the orthodox masters of the late seventeenth century, especially those of Wang Hui, Wang Yüan-ch'i and Wu Li, that Tung's noble ideals were consummated. These orthodox masters saw a great tradition of painting that continued with ever-renewed vigor from the time of Wang Wei (699-759)—the supposed originator of the Southern School in landscape painting—to their own time, almost exactly a thousand years. In the surviving ancient masterpieces of art they saw an unbroken historical thread of human genius, an irrefutable, visible proof of man's immortality. To them, the study of ancient models represented the only effective way of expanding and liberating the mind. By studying and mastering the ancient alternatives, an artist learned to conjure up images that captured and revealed nature's secrets. A true master, according to Tung Ch'i-ch'ang, was one who successfully confronted the dual challenge of history and nature: one

[20] For this and other quotations from Tung Ch'i-ch'ang, see my article "Tung Ch'i-ch'ang and the Orthodox Theory of Painting," *National Palace Museum Quarterly*, vol. II, no. 3, January 1968, pp. 1-26.

who had "read ten-thousand books and travelled ten-thousand miles."

While the orthodox theory eventually produced rigidity and stagnation in later Ch'ing painting, its earlier proponents were inspired reformers who, through fervent study "in pursuit of antiquity," each found a powerful style of his own. As Tung pointed out, true correspondence (*ho*) to ancient principles could come about only through individual metamorphosis (*pien*); the voice of the ancients was heard only by one who had found it in himself. The new paintings in the Morse Collection illustrate three kinds of "correspondence through metamorphosis" that proved essential to the creative experience of the orthodox masters.

II

Wang Hui's "Snow Clearing" (No. 30), dated 1669, which shows the Li Ch'eng idiom, represents an important departure from the narrow range of Tung Yüan and Chü-jan derived idioms favored by Tung Ch'i-ch'ang and the two older Wangs, Wang Shih-min and Wang Chien. In accord with their growing interest in calligraphic expression, the leading Yüan masters and their Ming followers all favored the calligraphic idiom of Tung Yüan and Chü-jan. Tung Ch'i-ch'ang had downgraded descriptive skill insisting that "in painting it is better to be [descriptively] obscure rather than obvious."

Ever since the fourteenth century, the Li Ch'eng idiom had been considered the antithesis of that of Tung Yüan and Chü-jan. Unlike the rolling masses of Tung and Chü which can be carried out with round calligraphic brushstrokes, the Li Ch'eng idiom, with its jagged "devil face" rock formation and spiky "crab-claw" wintry branches, demanded of the artist more descriptive skill than calligraphic power. Wang Hui in his "great synthesis" was trying to embrace the whole spectrum of painting's great tradition from the abstract and calligraphic to the descriptive and decorative. He wrote: "Painting has its obvious and obscure aspects. These are like the two wings of a bird; neither can be employed singly at the expense of the other. When the obvious and the obscure are equally perfected, a spirited 'breath' [*ch'i*] will emerge." By the late 1660's, he had mastered the calligraphic idiom of Huang Kung-wang (No. 12). In 1667, he made his first serious study of the Li Ch'eng idiom.[21] In the "Snow Clearing" of 1669 (No. 30), we see a perfectly

[21] See handscroll dated 1667, as illustrated in *Shi Ō Go Un*, Hakubundō, Osaka, 1919, plates 11-12.

controlled lyrical composition. Over a frozen stream, winding peaks clad in deep snow gradually fade into the distance. Through the filigree pattern of wintry branches, temple structures and a solitary pavilion are seen nestled in the mountain folds. The snowscape is held in enchanted stillness; the rocks and trees sing and dance in a joyous rhythm. Tints of reddish brown are lightly scattered among foliage along banks and cliffs. These vestiges of the fall also foretell the coming of spring.

A complete picture of Wang Hui's stylistic development can now be seen in the dated paintings by Wang Hui in the Morse Collection. In his landscape of 1660 in the style of Huang Kung-wang (No. 12) and in that of 1664 after Chü-jan and Wang Meng (No. 13) the calligraphic "hemp" strokes are the kinetic carriers of the "breath-force" (ch'i-shih), while in the 1669 scroll in the manner of Li Ch'eng it is the contour line of the convoluted rocks and trees that suggests movement. The Li Ch'eng idiom enabled him to describe and capture the more obvious charms of nature. In 1669 he also painted the "T'ai-hang Mountain" handscroll (No. 14) in the "rain-drop" idiom of Kuan T'ung and Fan K'uan. But both the Li Ch'eng and Kuan T'ung idioms represented only departures from the orthodox way. In his large landscape after Chü-jan, dated 1672 (No. 15), he discovered the key to his "great synthesis," which he confidently demonstrated in the album of 1673 presented to his teacher Wang Shih-min (No. 16). From his primary calligraphic formula of Chü-jan in the 1673 album (No. 16-A) came the subsequent leaves in the manners of Tung Yüan, Huang Kung-wang and Wang Meng (No. 16-B, D, F). The hanging scroll after Wu Chen, dated 1675 (No. 17), stems from the same calligraphic formula. The more descriptive and decorative leaves of the 1673 album, in the manners of Li Ti (?), Ts'ao Chih-po, Wang Shen, Li Ch'eng and Kuo Hsi (No. 16-C, E, H, J, K, L), on the other hand, were all derived from the Li Ch'eng idiom. Finally in the 1680's and 1690's, Wang Hui achieved a personal synthesis by combining his earlier themes into a more stable pattern. The handscroll of 1692 in the manner of Wang Meng (No. 19) combines description of nature's charms with calligraphic brushwork. It was this style which catapulted him into great fame and popularity, and made him, between 1691 and 1698, the favorite painter of the K'ang-hsi Emperor.

III

Unlike Wang Hui who was a commoner without a literary degree, Wang Yüan-ch'i (1642-1715), a grandson of Wang Shih-min, was born into a great scholar-official family. He passed his *chin-shih* degree in 1670, in his twenty-ninth year. In 1700 he was appointed adviser for the K'ang-hsi emperor's art collections. In 1705, as a lecturer in the Han-lin academy, he was made editor in chief of the *P'ei-wen-*

31a. Detail of No. 31

Fig. 8

chai shu-hua-p'u, an encyclopedic collection of writings on calligraphy and painting in one hundred volumes, which was completed in 1708.

Thus in family training and subsequent career, Wang Yüan-ch'i was a more typical amateur-scholar-painter than Wang Hui. The "Wang-ch'uan Villa" of 1711 (No. 31), a handscroll more than 18 feet long, took him nine months to complete. It was based on the 1617 engraved version of the famous "Wang-ch'uan" composition attributed to Wang Wei (Fig. 8). Wang Yüan-ch'i's scroll begins with twenty poems by Wang Wei describing the scenes illustrated in the painting. At the end of the painting, a long inscription tells how and why he did this work: "I acquired a popular stone engraving [of Wang Wei's composition]. Using the poems found in [Wang Wei's] collected works as a reference, I made this scroll with my own ideas, so that it is different from a copy of 'physical likeness' [*hsing-ssu*] by a professional painter. . . ."

In his introduction to *Gardens in Chinese Art,* Wango H. C. Weng points out that "Wang-ch'uan [is] a summation of the private domains of all scholars. Every garden owner would like to see something of 'Wang-ch'uan' around him."[22] Just as the subject matter of the Wang-ch'uan scroll epitomized the poet-scholar's way of life, so its composition was considered by the orthodox masters as the fountainhead of a thousand years of painting history. Wang Yüan-ch'i, for instance, wrote of the styles of Chao Meng-fu and Wang Meng as follows:

> Wang Meng's brushwork . . . was unexcelled. His early works resembled those of his uncle Chao Meng-fu, both men being influenced by Wang Wei's *Wang-ch'uan-t'u.* Later, Wang Meng discovered a new source for his brush and ink in Tung Yüan and Chü-jan. Thereafter he changed his family method, undergoing a series of astonishing stylistic metamorphoses. Yet in essence, he had merely used Wang Wei as his basis, while learning [to make] fresh applications with Tung and Chü's method.[23]

Wang Wei's Wang-ch'uan composition existed only in copies. In order to distinguish his work "from a copy of 'physical likeness' by a professional painter," a

[22] *Gardens in Chinese Art,* an exhibition at China House Gallery, New York, March 21 to May 26, 1968, p. 8.

[23] *Yü-ch'uang man-pi* in *Hua-hsüeh hsin-yin* edition, vii/25a-b.

more creative student of the composition must, in Wang Yüan-ch'i's words, "make the scroll with [his] own ideas." Technically, Tung Ch'i-ch'ang described the Wang-ch'uan scroll as being "largely without [rubbed] texture strokes, having only hook-like lines [*kou*] and ink wash."[24] This skeletal linear technique was exaggerated in the engraved version (Fig. 8), which gave Wang Yüan-ch'i his clue. Just as Tung Ch'i-ch'ang had turned the Huang Kung-wang idiom into a calligraphic formula of "[filling] concave and convex forms [with] straight texture strokes," Wang treated the Wang-ch'uan motif as a calligraphic combination of Huang Kung-wang and Wang Meng, with thin and wiry, but tremendously energetic, outlines (*kou*) and texture strokes turning into a torrential outpouring of writhing, churning rock forms, which rise and fall like tall waves.

As appropriate to an archaistic T'ang composition, Wang Yüan-ch'i used a blue-and-green color scheme in his "Wang-ch'uan" (Color Plate). Unlike most of his orthodox colleagues who normally built a form first in black brushstrokes and ink-wash, then added a color-wash to the finished form, Wang Yüan-ch'i used his blues, mineral greens, browns and reds as integral parts of his forms, achieving tremendous structural complexity in his composition. He explained:

> The use of color is to supplement what is not done by brush and ink; it is also to enhance what is achieved by brush and ink. Nowadays people do not understand this. Colors are treated as merely colors, and brush and ink are left as brush and ink. [As a result, the colors] neither fit the structural force (*shih*) of the landscape, nor penetrate beyond the surface of the silk. One sees only harsh patches of red and green that are annoying and tiresome.
>
> The only remedy is not to treat colors as colors alone, but instead, emphasize the structural "breath" (*ch'i*) of the composition. As a painter gradually brings out the *yin* and *yang*, front and back [in a composition], colors are naturally enlivened by the "breath." This way [colors] will not float on the surface and will not coagulate, and will naturally become part of the design. This is not something that can be achieved in haste.[25]

[24] *Jung-t'ai pi-chi*, iv/32a.
[25] *Yü-ch'uang man-pi, loc. cit.*, vii/5a.

To a Western observer, certain passages of Wang Yüan-ch'i's "Wang-ch'uan" easily bring to mind Cézanne's watercolors. In both painters' works there is a tightness of organization and solidity of formal structure, a strong sense of surface rhythm and plastic design. Both employ a deliberate juxtaposition, a free interplay and fusion, of foreground and distant elements. Even Wang's shading and use of blue suggests a parallel with Cézanne's modulated passages. When Maurice Denis wrote: "Remember that a picture—before being a battle horse, a nude woman or an anecdote—is essentially a plane surface covered with colors assembled in a certain order," the same sentence, adding the word "landscape," might well have been used to describe Wang Yüan-ch'i's painting. Indeed, Wang and Cézanne seem to have occupied a comparable position in their respective painting traditions; each in his way representing the rejection of a traditional, rationalized spatial organization in favor of a formal construction in abstract space. From pre-T'ang through Yüan, the Chinese gradually developed an illusionistic structure in landscape painting, first by employing a systematic diminution of elements along the vertical picture-plane and a rationalized three-step progression into depth, and finally by achieving the integration of elements within a unified, described ground-plane. The Ming painters, however, emphasized the picture-plane as a continuous decorative surface. It was Tung Ch'i-ch'ang who, by turning landscape compositions into abstract "breath-force" movements, brought to realization the possibility of the free flow of forms and the dynamic interplay and fusion of near and far-distance elements in early Ch'ing painting. The archaic convention of ringed mountain motifs, which is used in the Wang-ch'uan scroll, now inspired Wang Yüan-ch'i to create a vast arterial system (*mo*) of interconnected mountain ranges, through which the cosmic "breath-force" flows with vigor and abandon. Solid rock forms dangle freely in space. Between the "rising-and-falling" and "opening-and-closing" of the mountains, pockets of space are filled with houses and other details of a more intimate scale, giving a feeling of great distance and depth.

Wang Yüan-ch'i's resemblance to Cézanne is, to be sure, only a superficial one. While Cézanne's landscape "renders [visual] sensations concrete by means of drawing and color," the basis of Wang's abstraction is Chinese calligraphy. Calligraphy is nonrepresentational, and yet in its movements it perfectly evokes nature's qualities and life-rhythms. As painting became more and more calligraphic after the Sung period, it increasingly de-emphasized the representational content in favor of the purely expressive. When Tung Ch'i-ch'ang stated that he was much more interested in the "wonders of brush and ink" than real landscape scenery, he had ceased to look for either natural image or narrative meaning in his art, and instead, treated landscape painting as pure poetry of form and movement, or, in short, as calligraphy. In calligraphy each form is composed of a definite set of brushstrokes, yet the execution of these brushstrokes remains a spontaneous physical act. The basic design is a familiar one, and yet each character grows and "happens," and the result in every instance is different and unique.

Wang Yüan-ch'i wrote:

> In painting, one needs to pay attention only to the "breath-force" (*ch'i-shih*) and general outline of the design. It is not necessary to represent beautiful scenery; nor is it important to follow old compositions. If one knows how to "open-and-close," "rise-and-fall," whenever the "veins" (*mo*) and connections turn or halt, wonderful scenery will naturally appear." [26]

Wang Yüan-ch'i's brushwork is blunt and crusty, as he wields his brush (in his own words) "as if it were a diamond club," a devastating weapon that leaves a mark as permanent and indelible as a shape hewn in stone. Though he did not follow exactly the old Wang-ch'uan composition, it was nonetheless important that he had the model in front of him when he made his handscroll in 1711. The existence of such a model, with a set of well-tested compositional motifs and variations, put him completely at ease, freeing his inventive energy for what he considered to be the main business of landscape painting, namely, the "opening-and-closing" and "rising-and-falling" of the "breath-force" in composition.

The term *ch'i-shih*, or "breath-force," derives from the concept of *shih*, "momentum" or "force," as it is used in calligraphy criticism of a much earlier period. The *Chiu-shih*, or "Nine Forces," an essay attributed to Ts'ai Yung (A.D. 132-192), sees calligraphy as consisting of a series of interacting, checking, balancing and redirecting forces. "To go left, begin by making a reverse motion toward the right. ... Pull back the brush when the force of the stroke is spent." [27] Each brushstroke is

[26] *Ibid.*, vii/3a.
[27] *P'ei-wen-chai shu-hua-p'u*, iii/1a.

like a reptile in motion, always "hiding its head" and "protecting its tail." Another essay, attributed to Wang Hsi-chih (321-379), compares a calligraphic composition to a battle plan: "Paper is the battle field, brush is sword and lance, ink is helmet and armor, water and inkstone are moat and wall. The heart and mind make the commanding general, and skill is the general's lieutenant. Composition is strategy. The flying brush determines the outcome: its movements are the general's commands, its twists and turns the battle's killing and slaughter."[28] Every calligrapher and painter, therefore, fights a battle on paper.

In an important essay in his *Yü-ch'uang man-pi,* Wang Yüan-ch'i discusses the principle of *lung-mo,* or "dragon vein," in landscape composition. The term, meaning giant, dragon-like "veins" or "arteries," refers to serpentine compositional movements in seventeenth-century landscape painting.[29] In his essay Wang Yüan-ch'i first acknowledges his debt to Wang Hui, who is said to be the first to have made the "dragon vein" principle explicitly clear, then goes on to explain that in a large composition, the principal "dragon vein" should be treated as the "basic principle" (*t'i*), while smaller passages of "opening-and-closing" and "rising-and-falling" may be used as "individual applications" (*yung*) of the same principle. The essay represents the best explanation of Wang Yüan-ch'i's Wang-ch'uan composition:

> The "dragon vein" represents the principal "breath-force" in a painting; its course may be oblique or symmetrical, rounded or fragmented, broken or continuous, hidden or apparent. This is the "basic principle." As for "opening-and-closing," when the elements range from above to below, their host-and-guest relationships are clearly arranged; sometimes the elements are knotted together, sometimes they are light and drifting away, with peaks turning around, paths winding back, clouds locking together, and watercourses parting their ways. All these come from the principle of "opening-and-closing." As for "rising-and-falling," when the elements move from near to far, their positions of facing each other or turning away will be clearly distinguished; sometimes the elements are

[28] *Ibid.,* iii/1b.
[29] See Susan Bush, "Lung-mo, K'ai-ho, and Ch'i-fu: Some Implications of Wang Yüan-ch'i's Three Compositional Terms," *Oriental Art,* viii/3, Autumn 1962, pp. 120-127.

high and peaked, sometimes they are flat and smooth, or they lean to either side, answering one another, with the top, the middle and the foot of the mountain properly balanced and matched. All these are "individual applications" [of the basic "dragon vein" principle].

If a student realizes that a painting must have a "dragon vein," but does not know how to master the "opening-and-closing" and "rising-and-falling," his painting will be knotty and tied up together and will not achieve in the end the desired "[breath-]force." On the other hand, if he knows all about "opening-and-closing" and "rising-and-falling," but fails to subordinate these to the principal "dragon vein," he will be like someone who minds the children but forgets the mother. When the "dragon vein" is forced, it is a fault; when the "opening-and-closing" is crowded or choked, shallow or exposed, it is a fault; when the "rising-and-falling" is clumsy or incomplete, it is a fault.

Furthermore, there is "opening-and-closing" and "rising-and-falling" both in a large composition and in its parts. These principles can be used either to simplify or elaborate [a composition], according to need. When the "dragon," in its many oblique or frontal, unified or broken, obscured or apparent, interrupted or continuous positions, is lively and vivid, the painting will be true. When one masters this thoroughly, small bits will naturally grow into large masses. How can such a painting fail to be wonderful?[30]

A dominant idea in Chinese painting is that the artist must not imitate nature, but should instead capture life's "breath" through graphic conventions. In his Wang-ch'uan scroll, Wang Yüan-ch'i freely departed from both nature and his model. Though the basic design is a familiar one, each detail is his own. As the founder of the scholar-painting tradition, Wang Wei was said to be the first to have made the principle of "breath-resonance-life-motion" the chief consideration in painting. Now Wang Yüan-ch'i created a great composition of "breath-movement-life-motion" with powerful "dragon veins." In achieving a "spiritual correspondence" with Wang Wei through individual "metamorphosis," Wang Yüan-ch'i inherited the eternal "lamp-flame" that illuminated the great orthodox tradition of painting.

[30] *Yü-ch'uang man-pi, loc. cit.*, vii/2a-3a. See also translation by O. Sirén, *Chinese Painting: Leading Masters and Principles*, London, 1958, V, p. 209.

IV

Wu Li (1632-1718) was born in the same year as Wang Hui, and in the same town, Ch'ang-shu. Of the leading orthodox painters of the early Ch'ing, his life alone suggests a poignant bond of loyalty with the individualist monk-painters Chu Ta and Tao-chi. His father died shortly after he was born, and he lived with his widowed mother through the turbulent years of the Manchu conquest. A withdrawn and introspective person, he studied Confucianism, then Buddhism, and finally Christianity. Two years after the death of his mother, in 1664, he developed a close friendship with a Buddhist priest, Mo-jung, who died in 1672. By 1676 he had become friendly with some Jesuit priests in Ch'ang-shu, particularly with one Father François de Rougemont.[31] He was baptized in 1681 under the name Simon-Xavier, and accompanied Father Philippe Couplet to Macao, where he entered the Society of Jesus the following year. Ordained as a priest in 1688 under the name A Cunha, he was sent in 1689 to do missionary work in Shanghai, where he died on February 24, 1718.

In Macao, he recorded the following impressions of Western culture:

> Their manners and customs run counter to our own. When we meet visitors in our country, we straighten our robes and hats; here they simply take off their hats on meeting someone. In writing and painting, the differences are just as striking: our characters are made by gathering dots and strokes, and the sound comes afterward; they begin with phonetics, then words, making lines by scattering hooks and strokes in a horizontal row. Our painting does not seek physical likeness [hsing-ssu], and does not depend on fixed patterns; we call it "divine" and "untrammeled." Theirs concentrates entirely on the problems of dark and light, front and back, and the fixed patterns of physical likeness. Even in writing inscriptions, we write on the top of a painting, and they sign at the bottom of it. Their use of brush is also completely different. It is this way with everything, and I cannot describe it all.[32]

---

[31] A painting by Wu Li, entitled *Hu-t'ien ch'un-se*, "Spring Colors in Lake and Sky," dated in that year, is dedicated to "Mr. Lu [Father de Rougemont] from the Far West."

[32] *Mo-ching hua-pa*, in *Hua-hsüeh hsin-yin* edition, iv/47a; see translation by Sirén, *op. cit.*, V, p. 192.

By all accounts, Wu Li appears to have been a lonely and unsocial person. He studied with Wang Hui under both Wang Shih-min and Wang Chien. According to a story, he terminated his friendship with Wang because of a famous painting, Huang Kung-wang's *Tou-ho mi-lin*, "Thick Woods in a Deep Valley." He was said to have remarked on that occasion that "Wang Hui is my friend, but *Tou-ho mi-lin* is my teacher. It is better to lose a friend than to be deprived of a teacher!" The story may be apocryphal; it nevertheless tells us something of the man. In his early years, according to his biographer Li Ti, he had to sell his paintings in order to support his mother. Yet in one of his colophons, he wrote stubbornly:

> When the ancient man excelled in literature, he did not ask to be recommended on account of it; when he was good in painting, he did not ask for appreciation or reward. He would say [in the words of Su Shih] that "literature reaches to my heart, and painting satisfies my own feelings. I may dress only in straw and eat only a coarse vegetable, but I will not try to please others." Neither a prince, nor a duke, nor an imperial relation could send for, nor command, his services, for everyone knew that such a man could be neither honored nor humiliated. The *tao* of brush and ink cannot be mastered by one who has not the *tao* in himself.[33]

As measured by the number of works produced by other orthodox painters, Wu Li's total output was small. Early in his career, however, he developed a distinctly personal style. The handscroll "Passing the Summer at the Thatched Hall of Ink-well" (No. 32) is dated 1679, two years before he was baptized. His inscription at the end of the scroll explains that he was alone in his study after a heavy late-spring rain, and he painted this scroll in the manner of an ancient master. The monochrome landscape, in an elegant silvery-grey tone, shows a scholar's cottage by a river which flows quietly between distant rice fields and graceful tall willows. A small bridge and footpath behind the trees leads to the walled-in and well-shaded retreat, where the master of the "Thatched Hall of Ink-well" sits reading in an armchair. The scholar's dwelling is a simple hut, behind which, on higher ground, is a library and a kiosk. A lily pond and a low fence separate the master's quarters from the servants' area to the left. The view from the master's front hall, extending beyond the lily

---

[33] *Ibid.*, iv/44a-b.

pond, takes in the rising boulders and dense bamboo grove toward the left of the scroll. A gusty breeze, blowing up the bamboo leaves, sends dense mountain mist streaming across the top of the scroll.

There is a dream-like quality about the painting: birds, trees, bamboo, mist, and even rocks, dance joyously around the scholar-hermit, who reigns in his quiet idyllic domain. Wu Li wrote:

> Human affairs, large or small, are like a dream. Is not painting also a dream? What I dream of are mountains, streams, grass and trees, and I dream with my brush and ink, and that is all.[34]

The "hemp" modeling pattern of the rocks in this painting, a combination of the manners of Huang Kung-wang, Wang Meng and Wu Chen, is distinctly Wu Li's personal style; it "[fills] concave and convex forms [with] straight texture strokes." Wu has an extraordinary eye for cool, ravishing, textured patterns silhouetted and suspended in space. He has also an exceptionally handsome calligraphic style in the manner of Su Shih (1036-1101) (No. 32, a), which uses a flat, oblique stroke that makes dazzling sharp turns and hooks. This brush style brings to his tree branches, patterns of drifting mist and bunched bamboo leaves a lively and sensuous effect. His stroke, carried out by an obliquely held brush with the brush point kept to one side, makes angular turns like those of a twisted or folded belt (No. 32, a). Its kinesthetic quality animates the whole picture. In a sweeping "dragon vein" movement intricately contrasting patterns of brushstrokes pour forth with both an athlete's vigor and a poet's gentle cadence. Toward the end of the scroll, the brushwork becomes increasingly bold and free. The receding vista is a series of delightful ideographic motifs.

Wu Li shows his orthodoxy by claiming to have painted this scroll "in the manner of an ancient master." But his style is an intensely personal one. The orthodox master, by submitting himself to the great tradition, expects, in return, to be glorified by it. Wu Li wrote:

> People of the Chin and Sung [of the Six Dynasties period] might not have all loved wine, but they used wine to escape from the troubles of their time. In the late Yüan period, people and scholars also used painting

---

[34] *Ibid.*, iv/45b.

as a means to escape from world involvement. Quietly they found satisfaction in themselves and spent their years amongst forests and streams.[35]

Wu Li, in turn, a Confucian, a Buddhist and a Christian, was in truth an orthodox individualist. By ordinary standards, the scholar-painter who turned a Christian mission worker was perhaps a somewhat unconventional and eccentric person. Yet his kind of eccentricity followed a well-recognized pattern in Chinese history of individual "withdrawal-and-return." By withdrawing from a less-than-acceptable world, he returned to the great scholarly tradition of spiritual independence which made him a man who "could be neither honored nor humiliated."

[35] *Ibid.*, iv/45a-b.

Catalogue

Numbers 30-31-32

by
Marilyn and Shen Fu

WANG HUI (1632-1717)

30   Snow Clearing. Landscape after Li Ch'eng.

> Dated 1669. Hanging scroll; ink and color on paper. Height: 1.108 m.; width: 0.355 m.

The artist's inscription in two lines and his seals are placed in the upper left corner:

> The year *chi-yu* [1669] on the 22nd day of *hsiao-ch'un* [tenth lunar month], on setting out for Pai-hsia [Nanking] in a boat at Pi-ling [Kiangsu], [I] did this *Li Ch'eng Hsüeh chi t'u* [Snow Clearing after Li Cheng] under candle-light.   Wu-mu shan-jen, Shih-ku-tzu, Wang Hui inscribed.

SEALS:

Wang Hui: *Wu-mu shan-ch'iao* (C & W, p. 68, no. 48) and *Wang Hui chih yin*, after his inscription.

Wang Chi-ch'ien (born 1907): *Wang Chi-ch'ien hai-wai so chien ming chi* and *Yin lu hsien shu-hua yin*, on lower left corner.

Unidentified: *Chu hsüeh nan sheng* and *Sung-chiang Li-shih Chung-chi chen-ts'ang yin*, on lower right corner.

196

No. 30

WANG YÜAN-CH'I (1642-1715)

31   Wang-ch'uan Villa

>   Dated 1711. Handscroll; ink and color on paper. Height: 0.357 m.; length: 5.451 m.

The painting itself is prefaced by a transcription by the artist of the twenty poems of Wang Wei on the subject of his Wang-ch'uan Villa. Anticipating the poems, there is a superscription on the silk mounting by Wu Hu-fan (born 1894?):

>   Wang [Yüan-ch'i, *hao*] Lu-t'ai, Ssu-nung's masterpiece—the Wang-ch'uan Villa scroll.

>   Accompanied by twenty poems on the Wang-ch'uan Villa in a complement of poetry and painting. [Seen] in the treasured collection of Mr. Wang in the Shuang-lin shu wu [Twin Grove Studio] at Mo-li.

>   Wu Hu-fan inscribed.

The twenty poems, composed in 5-character regulated *chüeh-chü*-style verse, are written in Wang Yüan-ch'i's characteristic *hsing* (semi-cursive) style. The original text is preceded by a brief introduction by the poet Wang Wei: [36]

>   My cottage was in the Wang-ch'uan Valley. My wanderings included many places: Meng-ch'eng Valley, Mount Hua-tzu, My Study Among Beautiful Apricot Trees, a Hill of Graceful Bamboo, Deer Forest Hermitage, Magnolia Hermitage, Rivers of Dogwood, a Path through Imperial Locust Trees, an Arbour beside the Lake, South Hill, Beside Lake Yi, Waves of Willow, At the Rapids of the Luan Family, the Stream of Powdered Gold, White Stone Bank, North Hill, My Hermitage in the Bamboo Grove, Hibiscus Hill, the Lacquer Tree Garden, and the Pepper Tree Garden. During that period, my good friend P'ei Ti and I composed poems at leisure:

There follow the twenty poems by Wang Wei:

[36] The translation of the following is taken from *Poems by Wang Wei*, translated by Chang Yin-nan and Lewis C. Walmsley (Japan, 1958), pp. 33-43, in which there is included an explanatory note and map of the region:

>   The river Wang-ch'uan, with head waters at the entrance to Mount Chiang, flows south of Lan-t'ien, Shensi province, through a deep valley into a large pool. Except for one narrow path, Mount Chiang abounds in precipices so no other passage can be followed. Several miles south, the mountains dwindle into a wide-open plain from which, looking back, one sees only the crowding peaks. Still further south are thirteen places noted for beautiful scenery; among them the Temple of Deer Forest that became Wang Wei's villa. (p. 34)

199

◄ 30a. Detail of No. 30,
actual size

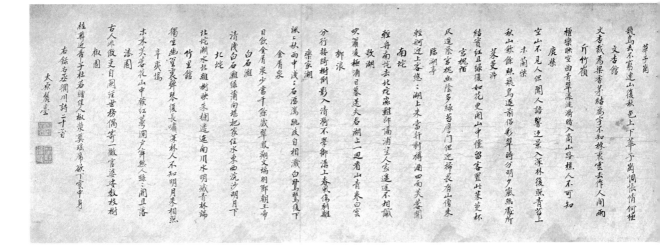

I   Meng-ch'eng Valley
    My new home stands sentinel at the entrance to Meng-ch'eng
    Where, of an ancient wood, only time-worn willows still remain . . .
    Who would come to live in this lonely place
    Unless to brood over the sorrows of the past?

II   Mount Hua-tzu
    Birds sail endlessly across the sky.
    Again the mountain range wears autumn's hue.
    As I wander up and down Mount Hua-tzu
    Deep shafts of sorrow pierce me!

III   My Study Among Beautiful Apricot Trees
    Slender apricot trees pillar my hermitage,
    Fragrant grasses thatch it;
    Mountain clouds drift through it—
    Clouds, could you not better make rain for needy peasants?

IV   A Hill of Graceful Bamboo
    Sandalwoods cast shadows across empty trails.
    Dark blue ripples race on the river.
    Secretly I enter the pathway to Mount Shang;
    Not even the woodcutter knows I am here.

V   Deer Forest Hermitage
    Through the deep wood, the slanting sunlight
    Casts motley patterns on the jade-green mosses.
    No glimpse of man in this lonely mountain,
    Yet faint voices drift on the air.

VI   Magnolia Hermitage
The autumn hills hoard scarlet from the setting sun.
Flying birds chase their mates,
Now and then patches of blue sky break clear . . .
Tonight the evening mists find nowhere to gather.

VII   Rivers of Dogwood
Green dogwood berries ripen to crimson
Though blossoms still star the branches.
Come friends! How can you bear not to stay in these mountains
And savor that rich red wine with me!

VIII   A Path Through Imperial Locust Trees
The narrow path hides beneath imperial locust trees;
Thick green mosses carpet the shaded earth.
While sweeping the courtyard, I keep watching the gate
Lest my friend, the mountain monk, should visit me.

IX   In an Arbor beside the Lake
My light skiff, garnished to welcome esteemed guests,
Leisurely floats along the lake.
On the shaded balcony we sit with our wine-cups
'mid lotus blossoms blooming in four directions.

X   South Hill
A small boat sails to South Hill;
North Hill is hard to reach—the river is wide.
On the far shore I see families moving,
Too distant to be recognized.

XI   Beside Lake Yi
Where the lake ends, she sits now playing her flute.
At dusk she bade farewell to her husband.
Wistfully she stares across the water,
Watching a white cloud rolling up the blue mountain side.

XII   Waves of Willow
The swaying branches of the willow row mingle their silken garments in
       caresses.
Reflected shadows ripple the clear water.
Be not like those willows weeping on the imperial embankment
Which sadden people parting on the cold spring wind . . .

XIII   At the Rapids of the Luan Family
Under the spatter of October rain
The shallow water slides over slippery stones;
Leaping waves strike each other
And frightened, the egret dares not dive for fish.

XIV   The Stream of Powdered Gold
He who drinks daily from the Stream of Powdered Gold
Shall live at least a thousand years!
Then he will be presented to the Jade Emperor,
Riding beneath a plumed canopy in a carriage drawn by soaring blue
      phoenixes and spirited young dragons.

XV   White Stone Bank
White Stone Bank River, shallow, clear,
Meanders past a sparse handful of rushes.
Families on the east and west banks
Wash silk in the silver moonlight.

XVI   North Hill
North Hill stands out above the lake
Against thick evergreens gleams startlingly a vermilion gate.
Below, South River zig-zags toward the horizon,
Glistening, here and there, beyond the tree-tops of the blue forest.

XVII   My Hermitage in the Bamboo Grove
Deep in the bamboo grove, sitting alone,
I thrum my lute as I whistle a tune.
No one knows I am in this thicket
Save the bright moon looking down on me.

XVIII   Hibiscus Hill
The blossoms on high hibiscus boughs
Fling crimson through the mountains.
Families no longer live in this deserted valley,
Yet season after season the hibiscus still blooms in profusion.

XIX   The Lacquer Tree Garden
The keeper of the Lacquer Tree Garden was no proud official:
That old sage knew nothing of worldly matters.
When by chance, he received this low-ranking office,
He sauntered about lazily caring for a few gnarled trees!

XX   The Pepper Tree Garden
    With a flask of cinnamon wine, we welcome the daughters of Emperor Yao;
    To the Beautiful Goddess, we present fragrant grasses
    And we greet the Prince of the Clouds
    With a peppery drink and delectable feast.

Wang Yüan-ch'i's own inscription follows the painting on a separate sheet of paper:

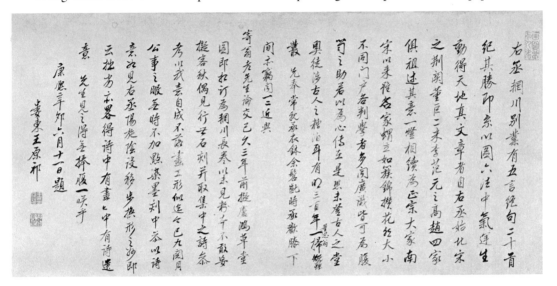

On the right is Yu-ch'eng's [Wang Wei's] Wang-ch'uan villa. Having written twenty poems of five-word regulated verse to describe the scenes, [Wang Wei] also painted this composition. In the art of the Six Principles [*i.e.*, painting], it was Yu-ch'eng who first mastered [the secret of] "breath-movement-life-motion," capturing the true composition of the universe. Ching [Hao], Kuan [T'ung], Tung [Yüan], Chü- [jan], the two Mis [Mi Fu and Mi Yu-jen], Li [Ch'eng] and Fan [K'uan] of the Northern Sung, as well as Kao [K'o-kung], Chao [Meng-fu] and the Four Masters [Huang Kung-wang, Wu Chen, Ni Tsan and Wang Meng] of the Yüan, all followed [Wang Wei's] ideas, each inheriting the "lamp-flame" and becoming a great master of the Orthodox tradition. Since the Southern Sung period, there have been a great many known painters competing with each other like flowers on a piece of brocade, each of them of a different stature, school and tradition. Though a student might broaden himself by using these different traditions to fill out [his education], were he to mistake this as his sole training, he would then have attained merely the dregs of the ancient tradition, and not its inner essence.

203

During the three hundred years of the Ming dynasty, only Tung Ssu-weng [Tung Ch'i-ch'ang] succeeded in sweeping away the web of confusion. My late grandfather Feng-ch'ang [Wang Shih-min] personally inherited the [orthodox] mantle [from Tung]. As I used to attend [my grandfather] in my youth, I have learned a few things [about painting]. In recent years, I have become acquainted with the elderly gentleman Chi-weng. When I painted for him Lu Hung's *Ts'ao-t'ang t'u*, about three years ago, I had promised that I would someday paint also the long handscroll composition Wang-ch'uan [by Wang Wei]. Since I had not then had access to a reliable sketch of the composition, I did not dare to tackle it from ignorance. Last autumn, I acquired a popular stone engraving [of the composition]. Using the poems found in [Wang Wei's] collected works as a reference, I made this scroll with my own ideas, so that it is different from a copy of "physical likeness" [*hsing-ssu*] by a professional painter. Nine whole months have since passed. During every leisure hour away from official duties, I have worked on it. By adding poetry to the ink engraving, I have been able to see the wonders of Yu-ch'eng's designs of *yang* and *yin*, their ever-changing forms and steps. Though some may think that my work is clumsy and inferior, I believe that it has captured some of [Wang Wei's] idea of "painting in poetry and poetry in painting." Will not the Master [Chi-weng] have a chuckle over this?

    K'ang-hsi, *hsin-mao* [1711], the 6th moon, the 11th day.
    Inscribed by Wang Yüan-ch'i of Lou-tung.

Following Wang Yüan-ch'i's own inscription, there are twelve colophons attached to an additional length of paper. The first colophon by Huang I (1744-1802) reads:

Shih-shih tao-jen [Wang Yüan-ch'i] has grasped the *ch'i* [breath] and *yün* [resonance] of Tung [Yüan], Chü[-jan], Ni [Tsan] and Huang [Kung-wang]. He certainly is of the true heritage of the Southern School and hence suited to aspirations after Wang-ch'uan. Trusting his hand he completes a painting which is intrinsically antique. Old and hoary with a skeletal energy, we can imagine seeing the man himself. As to a precise and neat arrangement of the houses, cottages and figures, he wasn't originally adept at such a thing, so we needn't go into that further. When Yen-ts'un (unidentified) got this scroll, he sent it to me to enjoy for three months. Now I am about to return home, and so I inscribe [the work] and return it to him. Huang I of Ch'ien-t'ang [Chekiang].

Huang I's colophon

204

The second colophon by Wu Hu-fan (born 1894?) pays lengthy tribute to the unique quality of the scroll by drawing upon varied analogies from the human and natural worlds:

> Lu-t'ai Ssu-nung [Wang Yüan-ch'i] possesses sage powers and a mind of profound intuition. In the painting world he stands unique as a brilliant flag unfurled, and before and after him for a thousand years, he has surpassed the wonders of a mass of others to bring to completion this marvelous work. He [Wang Yüan-ch'i] himself said: "I have made this scroll with my own ideas, so that it is different from a copy of 'physical likeness' [*hsing-ssu*]." We can imagine how keen his concentration was as he was painting: he did not follow the path of the well-trodden, but amassed his energies, tempered his spirit and had eternity in mind. Hence we know this work is not of the kind to be found often. In the great inter-action of Heaven and Earth, Heaven concentrates the most excellent qualities: in the T'ang, there was Mo-chieh [Wang Wei], and in Mo-chieh there was the Wang-ch'uan composition. A thousand years later, and there is the interpretative brush of Lu-t'ai [Wang Yüan-ch'i] with Mo-chieh's Wang-ch'uan composition. This work has also come about as the result of the concentration of the most excellent qualities in permutations of Heaven and Earth. It is certainly not a thing which we may stumble upon accidentally.

> To have Mo-chieh's Wang-ch'uan composition in painting is like having Yu-chün's [Wang Hsi-chih's] Lan-t'ing hsü in calligraphy, or [Li] T'ai-po in poetry and Ch'ang-li [Han Yü] in prose; it is like moonlight over [Lake] Tung-t'ing, or the clouds along Wu-hsia [section of the Yangtze river], or the rain over the Hsiao-hsiang [River]—they are all wonders of which there can never be a second, and of which there must always be a one. [When] Lu-t'ai has his gifts and the moment in hand, the rich and the pale and the whole spectrum of light and hue are at his command. Therefore [his] subtlety in applying colors is not something we can often come upon even in our dreams. In every brushstroke and in every ink tone, in every tree and in every rock, that which is known as "the breath which can swallow [Lake] Yün-meng," and "the wave which can devastate a city,"—rushing and surging like the Ch'ang-chiang [Yangtze] and Huang-ho [Yellow river]—in one torrent it gushes forth for a thousand *li*. And should there be a great barricade or wall of iron, it could not be obstructed—[such is the power] which can be seen in equal measure in Li [Po's] verse, Han [Yü's] essays, Yu-chün's calligraphy and Mo-chieh's painting!

I myself have been painting for some thirty years and of the famous works which I have seen to authenticate, there have been some ten thousand paintings; of these, there have been a thousand works—large and small handscrolls, hanging scrolls and album leaves—of Lu-t'ai. When I examine his [Wang Yüan-ch'i's] life, his most profound respect has been accorded Ni [Tsan] and Huang [Kung-wang]; [but] his knowledge of them has been acquired through Feng-ch'ang [Wang Shih-min] and Ssu-weng [Tung Ch'i-ch'ang] and the Yüan sages. This scroll is an attempt to re-capture Mo-chieh, and he [Wang Yüan-ch'i] himself said: "[I] have grasped the meaning of 'in poetry there is painting, and in painting there is poetry.'" His [Wang Yüan-ch'i's] spirit [in the painting] resembles his [Wang Wei's] forms, and in not seeking a resemblance, there is resemblance. We might even look upon [it] as a work by Wang Wei himself. At the beginning of the scroll there are twenty poems on Wang-ch'uan, and at the end of the painting there is the seal *Mo-chieh hou shen* [the re-incarnation of Mo-chieh], which will serve to prove that the Ssu-nung was pleased with himself, and that my words are not idle.

Feng-ch'ang [Wang Shih-min] carried on as leader of the painting world for more than forty years after Ssu-weng [Tung Ch'i-ch'ang]. When Feng-ch'ang died, the Ssu-nung was forty years old. Feng-ch'ang once said: "As for grasping Ta-ch'ih's [Huang Kung-wang's] spirit [*shen*], there is Ssu-weng; as for grasping his forms [*hsing*], there am I; as for both spirit and form, they have been grasped alike by Lu-t'ai." Feng-ch'ang had already passed away thirty years when this scroll was finished. During these thirty years Lu-t'ai made great strides. What a pity Feng-ch'ang is no longer here to see [it].

Hu-fan says: "If Feng-ch'ang could be raised [from his grave] to see this scroll, [I] would not know what expressions of astonishment and what words of criticism he would offer his grandson. It seems suitable then that one born later such as I should hold such reverence and dare to call [this scroll] Wang Ssu-nung's masterpiece [*t'ien-hsia ti-i*]. May Chi-ch'ien, my pupil, guard well [this scroll] and treasure it always. In late spring of the year *chia-shen* [1944], Wu Hu-fan, on several perusals, respectfully recorded.

The following two colophons are brief notations after seeing the painting:

In a summer month of the year *chia-shen* [1944] looked at respectfully by Chao Shih-kang of Chin [(1872-1945), Ning-po, Chekiang].

In early autumn of the year *chia-shen* [1944], P'ao-chüan chü-shih, Wu Cheng seen at Wu.

The fifth colophon by Wu Tzu-shen (born 1894?) reads:

In the past twenty years I have seen more than a few long handscrolls by Lu-t'ai Ssu-nung. Of those which can partake of a seasoned refinement and a lofty brilliance, there is the *Hsi-shan ho pi* [Streams in a Mountain Setting] after the Four Yüan Masters [in the collection of] Shao Sung-lao of Ch'in-ch'üan, and the *Yen nan ch'un hsiao* [Spring dawn over Peaks and Rapids] in the I-kuan hsien [Total Enlightenment Studio], and most of all this scroll after the Wang-ch'uan composition. Chi-ch'ien, my "younger brother," who happened to come upon it, brought it out to show me. After satiating myself with looking, I am honored to place my name at the end, feeling especially overjoyed and deeply fortunate.

> Late in the year *chia-shen* [1944], written by the "later student" Wu Hua-yüan, who also saw it in company with Mr. Wang Po-yüan and my "sixth younger brother" Ssu-lan.

The sixth colophon by Hsü Pang-ta (contemporary) reads:

In the year *i-yu* [1945] on the *teng-hsi* [eve of candles] [I] went to the Twin Grove Studio and again saw the incomparably "divine" work of the Ssu-nung. Respectfully recording the year and the month, Hsin-yüan chü-shih, Hsü Pang-ta.

The following four colophons note only the date. The seventh by T'ang Yün (contemporary):

The 12th month of the year *i-yu* [1945] seen respectfully by T'ang Yün of Hang [chow].

The eighth colophon by Chang Ta-ch'ien (born 1899):

In the *chia-p'ing* [12th] month of the year *ping-hsü* [1946] seen by Chang Yüan of Shu [Szechuan] province.

The ninth colophon by Wang Ya-ch'en (born 1893):

In early autumn of the year *chi-ch'ou* [1949], seen by Wang Ya-ch'en.

The tenth colophon by Huang Chün-pi (born 1898):

In early autumn of the year *ping-wu* [1966] seen by Huang Chün-pi of Nan-hai [Canton].

The eleventh colophon by Kao I-hung (contemporary):

> In the 8th month of the year *ping-wu* [1966] I went with [Huang] Chün-pi, "my elder brother" to New York [City] and at the Twin Grove Studio was enriched by the perusal of the Ssu-nung's long handscroll. Unawares, I sighed looking at [something which would] end [all looks]! Respectfully recorded by the master of Lan-hsiang kuan [Orchid-scent residence], Kao I-hung.

The last colophon is by Ling Shu-hua (contemporary lady collector residing in France):

> In the 4th month of the spring of the year *ting-wei* [1967], Ling Shu-hua respectfully inscribes this to record this visual richness.

SEALS:

Wang Yüan-ch'i: *Yüan-ch'i mao ching* (C & W, p. 41, no. 47) and *Mo-chieh hou shen*, after the twenty poems; *Hsing yü yen hsia hui*, on first joint of the painting; *Shih-shih tao-jen* (C & W, p. 41, no. 32), on second joint of the painting; *Hua t'u liu yü jen k'an* (C & W, p. 42, no. 60), lower right corner before his inscription; *Wang Yüan-ch'i yin* (C & W, p. 41, no. 26) and *Lu-t'ai* (C & W, p. 41, no. 40), after his inscription.

Huang I (1744-1802): *Hsiao sung*, after his colophon.

Wu Hu-fan (born 1894?): *Wu Hu-fan yin* and *Ch'ing-an*, after his superscript; *Hu-fan tu hua*, lower left corner of painting; *Wu shih t'u-shu chi* and *Ta-ch'ih Fu-ch'un shan t'u i-chio jen-chia*, before his colophon; *Wu Hu-fan*, after his colophon.

Wu Tzu-shen (born 1894?): *Yen ling*, before his colophon; *Wu Hua-yüan yin* and *Tzu-shen*, after his colophon.

Wu Cheng (contemporary, deceased): *Wu Cheng chih yin*, after his colophon.

Chang Ta-ch'ien (born 1899): *Chang Yüan* and *Ta-ch'ien chü-shih*, after his colophon.

Wang Chi-ch'ien (born 1907): *Chen-tse Wang shih Chi-ch'ien shou-ts'ang chih yin* and *Huai-yün-lou chien-shang shu-hua chih chi*, on mounting before the painting; *Chi-ch'ien*, lower right corner of painting; *Huai-yün-lou* and *Wang shih Chi-ch'ien chen-ts'ang chih yin*, lower left corner of painting; *Wang Chi-ch'ien yin* and *Huai-yün-lou*, on silk mounting after the painting; *Tseng ts'ang Wang Chi-ch'ien ch'u*, lower left corner following Wang Yüan-ch'i's inscription; *Shuang-lin shu-wu*, lower right corner of painting.

This well-known painting has been published most recently in *Great Drawings of All Time* (1962), vol. IV, p. 905, and in *Gardens in Chinese Art* (1968), p. 8. Before entering the collection of Mr. C. C. Wang, the scroll was owned by Mr. Hsü Pang-ta, who left no collector's seals on the work.

31a. Detail of No. 31
actual size

WU LI (1632-1718)

32   Passing the Summer at the Thatched Hall of Inkwell.
Mo-ching Ts'ao-t'ang Hsiao-hsia t'u.

>Dated 1679. Handscroll, ink on paper. Height: 0.363 m.; length: 2.726 m.

The label of a previous mounting has been remounted onto new silk to precede the painting and is entitled and sealed by a former owner Ku Wen-pin (1811-1889):

>Wu [Li, *hao*] Yü-shan presented the painting Passing the Summer at the Inkwell Thatched Hall to Hsü Ch'ing-yü.
>
>>Collected and authenticated by the master of the Kuo yün lou [Passing-cloud Pavilion] [Ku Wen-pin].

The painting is executed on two sheets of paper with the artist's seals on the join. At the end of the painting, Wu Li has left a four-line inscription which is signed and also impressed with his seals:

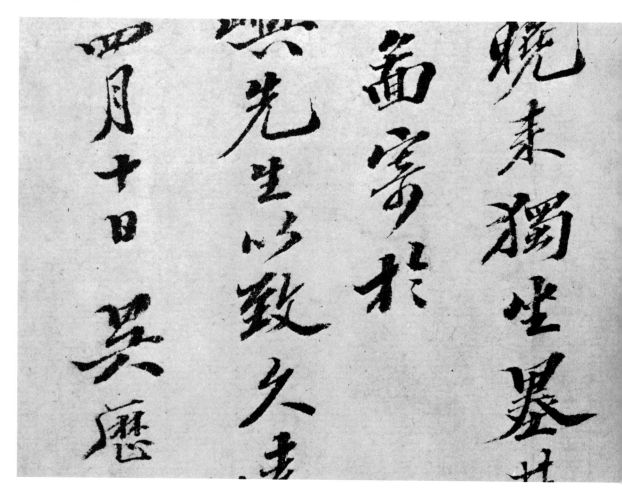

At the first clearing of the spring rain, [I] sat alone in the early dawn at the Ink-well Thatched Hall; and taking the compositions of "Passing the Summer" of the ancients as my teacher, [I painted this] to send to Mr. [Hsü] Ch'ing-yü of Pi-ling [Kiangsu] in order to gratify my long yearnings after him. The 10th day of the 4th month of the year *chi-wei* [1679]. Wu Li.

Five colophons are appended on a separate sheet of paper at the end of the scroll. The first by Sun Yüan-hsiang (1760-1829) reads:

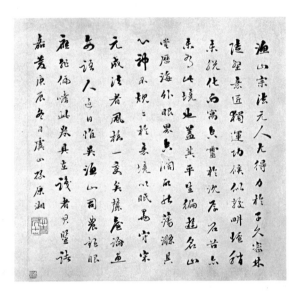

Yü-shan's [Wu Li's brush] method follows the tradition of the Yüan masters, [and while] gaining especial force from Tzu-chiu's [Huang Kung-wang] *Mi-lin tou-ho* [Thick Woods in a Deep Valley], his conception and artistic intention have been realized with independence. When compared to Keng-yen [Wang Hui, from the point of view of] training and maturity, he is not yet as liberated; nevertheless, he has been able to lodge a radiant spaciousness into the weighty character—and this is something which Shih-ku [Wang Hui] has not yet been able to attain! This is probably due to [Wu Li's] having roamed all the famous mountains all his life and wandered "beyond the ocean" [a reference to Wu Li's sojourn to Macao]. The scope of his vision has breadth, and so he has been able to purify his spirit and not restrict himself to a limited sphere. When comparing him to those who have confined their methods only to the Sung and Yüan masters—what a complete metamorphosis of style has taken place! Whenever Lu-t'ai [Wang Yüan-ch'i] talks about painting, he

213

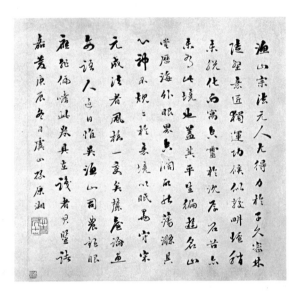

← 32 a. Detail of Wu Li's inscription,
twice actual size

says: "Nowadays, there is only Wu [Li] Yü-shan." Given the Ssu-nung's [Wang Yüan-ch'i] experienced eye, [this statement] ought not to be a whimsical pleasantry. The scroll is here, those who know can see for themselves. A winter's day of the year *keng-ch'en* [1820] of the Chia-ch'ing era. Sun Yüan-hsiang.

The second colophon by Ku Wen-pin is prefaced by two long passages in rhyme-prose [*tz'u*] style, not translated here. These *tz'u* take the form of linked verse taken from the respective collected *tz'u* of the two poets Wu Wen-ying (*hao* Meng-ch'uang, 1205?-1270?) and Chang Yen (*hao* Yü-t'ien, 1248-1320?) to form two "new compositions. The colophon reads:

> With the preceding *tz'u* written to the tune of *To li*, [I] inscribed Wu [Li] Yü-shan's picture on the Thatched Hall of Inkwell. Yü-shan's paintings and Shih-ku's [Wang Hui] were of equal fame. [Wu Li] did not regard the matter of painting for others lightly, therefore those [paintings] which are extant today are few and far between. At his abode there was the Mo-ching [the inky-black well] of Yen-tzu (the favorite disciple of Confucius), so [he, Wu Li] adopted [it] as his *hao* [sobriquet or studio name]. This scroll emulates the idea of the compositions on "passing the summer" by the ancients. And while he himself entitled it *Mo-ching ts'ao-t'ang* [Inkwell Thatched Hall, it] also resembles the *Wang-ch'uan* composition of Mo-chieh [Wang Wei] and the *Shan-chuang* [Lung-mien, the Mountain Hermitage of the Sleeping Dragon] by Po-shih [Li Kung-lin]. According to the *chi-wei* [1679] date, the revered gentleman was 48 years old. I also have in my possession his [Wu Li's] composition on the P'en River (a tributary of the Yangtze River near Chiu-chiang), which was made in the year *hsin-yu* [1681], a difference of two years. The brushwork [in both works] is similar in every respect and both were presented to [Hsü] Ch'ing-yü. The *Ssu-yü* [rank of Adviser-in-Attendance] Mr. Hsü, whose name is Chih-chien, was on terms of deepest friendship with him. [The painting] is a work presented to an intimate, so it is right that he should execute it with such keen insight as this. After the full moon [*chi-wang*] on the 7th month of the year *ping-yin* [1866] in the 5th year of the T'ung-chih reign period. Ken-an chü-shih, Ku Wen-pin recorded at the Passing-cloud Pavilion.

The third colophon by Yeh Kung-ch'o (contemporary) reads:

> Formerly Shih-ku [Wang Hui] and Mo-ching [Wu Li] were equally famous, but I had always praised Wu and disdained Wang because their character and intellect differ so greatly. Mo-ching's conversion to Catholicism can be likened to escapism from society: he embraces the concept of allegiance to no political

monarch. This is a belief which matches that of Hsü Ch'ing-yü. Theirs is by no means a superficial friendship. Their literary correspondence especially demonstrates this as well. Hence, the unusual excellence of his execution is certainly something to be treasured.

> The 4th month of the 36th year of the Chinese Republic [1947],
> Yeh Kung-ch'o inscribed, enriched by looking [at it].

The fourth colophon by Fei Nien-tz'u (1855-1905) merely records the date of perusal:

> The 6th month of the year *i-shih* [1905] in the Kuang-hsü reign period, seen by Fei Nien-tz'u of Wu-chin [Kiangsu].

The fifth and concluding colophon by Chang Ta-ch'ien (born 1899) reads:

> Of the authentic works of Yü-shan [Wu Li], [I] have seen several in the past twenty years: *T'ao p'u sung chü* [Pines and Chrysanthemum of T'ao Ch'ien] and *K'uai-chi shu wu* [K'uai-chi studio] are both in the style of [Wang Meng] Shan-ch'iao. There is also *Hsing-fu-an kan chiu t'u* [Reminiscing on the Past at the Hsing-fu Retreat] executed for Sheng Yü shang-jen, which is in the "blue and green" manner after Ou-po and his son [Chao Meng-fu and Chao Yung]. These [three] works are all the world's great treasures. This [painting] depicting the whiling-away of summer at his own thatched cottage was presented to Hsü Ch'ing-yü. The ink [blends] harmoniously and the pale [washes suggest] far distances, while the force of the brushwork is engulfed by the whole momentum [of the picture]. The work completely emulates Yen Wen-kuei and lies above and beyond the three paintings mentioned. Perhaps it is because Ch'ing-yü is such a complement to him that this is a work only for an intimate and kindred spirit. The first day [*shou*] of the 11th month of the year *ping-hsü* [1946]; Mr. [Wang] Nan-p'in took [the painting] out [for me] to see and asked [me] to inscribe it. Chang Ta-ch'ien [*hao*] Yüan of Shu [Szechuan] province.

SEALS:

Wu Li: *Yü-shan Wu Li* (C & W, p. 651, no. 19), on lower right corner of painting; *Yen-ling* and *Li*, on joint of the painting; *Yü-shan* and *Wu Li*, after his inscription.

Sun Yüan-hsiang (1760-1829): *Hsin-ch'ing chü-shih* and *Hsü-hsi*, after his colophon.

Ku Wen-pin (1811-1889): *Kuo-yün-lou-chu* (C & W, p. 724, no. 7), after the inscription on the label; *Ku Tzu-shan mi ch'ieh yin* (C & W, p. 630, no. 6), on right edge of painting; *Ku Lin-shih*, on lower left corner of painting; *Ku Wen-pin yin* and *Tzu-shan*, after his colophon.

Fei Nien-tz'u (1855-1905): ? *-chai*, after his colophon.

Yeh Kung-ch'o (contemporary): *Hsia-an*, after his colophon.

Chang Ta-ch'ien (born 1899): *Chang Yüan chih yin* and *Ta-ch'ien*, after his colophon.

Wang Chi-ch'ien (born 1907): *Chen tse Wang shih Chi-ch'ien shou-ts'ang yin* and *Huai-yün-lou chien-shang shu-hua chih chi*, on silk mounting before the painting.

Wang Nan-p'in (Hongkong dealer): *Wang Nan-p'in yin*, on right corner of painting.

Unidentified: *Yü-chai* and *Ch'ing-fen shu-wu*, on right corner of painting; *Chu-chuang chien ts'ang*, on left corner of painting.

The painting has been in the collections of Messrs. Ku Wen-pin, Wang Nan-p'in and C. C. Wang before entering the Morse Collection. Publications of the work include Osvald Sirén, *Chinese Paintings: Leading Masters and Principles* (1958), vol. VI, pls. 408-409-B; *Chung-kuo Hua-chia Ts'ung-shu* (1962), in which author Shao Lo-yang mentions the work as Wu Li's masterpiece; and most recently in Wango H. C. Weng, *Gardens in Chinese Art* (1968).

梅雨初晴晚來獨坐墨井草堂上师
士人消夏畫寫於
毘陵青嶼先生以致久遠之懷
己未年四月十日 吳歷

Glossary

with Chinese Characters
by Lucy L. Lo

An Ch'i 安岐

Autumn Colors among Streams and Mountains, see *Ch'i-shan ch'iu-se t'u*

Autumn Colors on the Ch'iao and Hua Mountains, see *Ch'iao Hua ch'iu-se t'u*

Ch'a Shih-piao 查士標

Ch'an 禪

Chang Ching ssu-yin shen-ting chen-ts'ang
張經私印審定珍藏

Chang Chü-ch'ü (Chang Yü) 張句曲

Chang-hou 章侯

Chang Hsiao-ssu 張孝思

Chang Hsiung 張熊

Chang Jo-ai 張若靄

Chang Jo-ch'eng 張若澄

Chang Ta-ch'ien 張大千

Chang Ta-yung 張大鏞

Chang T'ing-yü 張廷玉

Chang Tse-chih 張則之

Chang Yen (*hao* Yü-t'ien) 張炎

Chang Yü 張雨

Chang Yüan 張爰

Ch'ang-chou Wang Shih-shin Yüeh-hsien chen-ts'ang 長洲王時新月軒珍藏

Ch'ang-li 昌黎

Ch'ang-men fu 長門賦

Ch'ang-shu 常熟

Chao Ch'ien-li 趙千里

Chao Ling-jang 趙令穰

Chao Meng-fu 趙孟頫

Chao Po-chü 趙伯駒

Chao Shih-kang 趙時棡

Chao Yung 趙雍

Che 浙

Chen chi 真寄

Chen-ting Wang-shih 真定王氏

Chen-tse Wang-shih Chi-ch'ien so-ts'ang yin
震澤王氏季遷所藏印

Chen-tse Wang-shih Pao-wu-t'ang t'u hua chi 震澤王氏寶武堂圖畫記

Ch'en Ch'eng 陳誠

Ch'en Ch'ung-pen 陳崇本

Ch'en Ch'ung-pen k'ao-ts'ang yin
陳崇本攷藏印

Ch'en Hsü Nai-p'u 臣徐乃普

Ch'en Hui 臣翬

Ch'en Hung-shou 陳洪綬

Ch'en Hung-shou yin 陳洪綬印

Ch'en K'uei-ling 陳夔麟

Ch'en K'uei-lung 陳夔龍

Ch'en Shao-shih hsin-hai hou chien-ts'ang
陳少石辛亥後鑑藏

Ch'en Wen yin-chi 臣汶印記

Cheng-shu 正朮

Ch'eng chi-i 程集義

223

Ch'eng-ch'in-wang　成親王

Ch'eng Sui　程邃

Ch'eng-te　承德

Chi-ch'ien　季遷

Chi-ch'ien chen-ts'ang　季遷珍藏

Chi-ch'ien hsin-shang　季遷心賞

Chi-hsia i-ch'ing　戲暇怡情

chi lo yü hua (lodge joy in painting)
　　寄樂於畫

Chi-yang Sun-shih　暨陽孫氏

Ch'i　齊

ch'i (breath)　氣

ch'i-fu (rise-and-fall)　起伏

Ch'i-shan ch'iu-se　溪山秋色

Ch'i-shan ho pi　溪山合璧

Ch'i-shan hsing-lü t'u　溪山行旅畫

Ch'i-shan yüeh-kuan t'u　溪山樾館畫

ch'i-shih (breath-force)　氣勢

ch'i-yün-sheng-tung (breath-resonance-life-
　　motion)　氣韻生動

Ch'i tzu　七子

Chia-ch'ing yü-lan chih pao　嘉慶御覽之寶

Chia-ho Yao-shih　嘉禾姚氏

Chia-kuan (masterpiece)　甲觀

Chia-shen　甲申

Chiang-chu ch'iu-ch'ing　江渚秋晴

Chiang-kuan hsiao-chi　江關曉霽

Chiang-nan　江南

Chiang-shan (Ta Chung-kuang)　江山

Chiang-shang wai-shih　江上外史

Ch'iao Hua ch'iu-se t'u　鵲華秋色畫

Chieh-ch'ao　解嘲

Chieh-tzu-yüan hua-chuan　芥子園畫傳

Chien-pai-chai　堅白齋

Ch'ien-an　倩盫

Ch'ien-ch'ing-kung chien-ts'ang pao
　　乾清宮鑑藏寶

Ch'ien Ku　錢穀

Ch'ien Ku ssu-yin　錢穀私印

Ch'ien-lung chien-shang　乾隆鑑賞

Ch'ien-lung yü-lan chih pao
　　乾隆御覽之寶

Ch'ien-lung yü-wan　乾隆御玩

Ch'ien Shu-pao shih　錢氏叔寶

Ch'ien-t'ang　錢塘

Ch'ien-tzu-wen　千字文

Ch'ien Yün-chih　錢允治

Chih-ting ssu-yin　之定私印

Ch'ih-an　遲盫

Ch'ih-an shu-hua　遲盫書畫

Ch'ih-weng (Huang Kung-wang)　癡翁

Chin-ch'ang (Soochow)　晉昌

Chin-ch'ing (Wang Shen)　晉卿

Chin-ling (Nanking) 金陵

chin-shih 進士

Chin-t'an 金壇

ch'in (zither) 琴

Ch'in-ch'uan 琴川

Ch'in-lai 琴來

Ch'in Tsu-yung 秦祖永

Ching Hao 荊浩

Ching-ch'i 荊溪

Ching-k'ou 京口

Ching-su-shih so-ts'ang 景蘇室所藏

ch'ing (feeling) 情

Ch'ing-ch'i chien-ting 晴谿鑒定

Ch'ing-fen shu-wu 清芬書屋

Ch'ing-ho Chang Jo-ai Ch'ing-lan shih chen-
　wan chih chang

清河張若靄晴嵐氏珍翫之章

Ch'ing-hsi 慶喜

Ch'ing-hui 清暉

Ch'ing-hui lao-jen 清暉老人

Ch'ing-hui-lao-jen shih-nien pa-shih-yu-i

清暉老人時年八十有一

Ch'ing-hui-lao-jen shih-nien pa-shih-yu-erh

清暉老人時年八十有二

Ch'ing-hui tseng-yen 清暉贈言

Chiu-chiang 九江

Chiu-shih 九勢

Ch'iu Kung 裘公

Ch'iu-shan wen-tao t'u 秋山問道圖

Cho-cheng-yüan 拙政園

Chou Erh-yen 周而衍

Chou Liang-kung 周亮公

Chou Tso-hsin yin 周祚新印

Chu-ch'ih pi-wan 竹癡祕玩

Chu-chuang chien-ts'ang 竹莊鑑藏

Chu hsüeh nan sheng 竹雪南生

Chu-shih-t'ing 煮石亭

Chu Ta 朱耷

Chu Ting-fu 朱定甫

Chü-c'hü shan-chuang 句曲山莊

Chü-jan 巨然

Chü Wu i-min 句吳逸民

Ch'ü-an p'i-ai pu-chia pu-shih

遽庵癖愛不假不市

Ch'ü ch'iao ya ch'ü 臞樵雅趣

ch'ü-ku (to pursue antiquity) 趨古

Ch'u Sui-liang 褚遂良

Ch'u-tz'u 楚辭

Ch'uan-ching-t'ang chen-ts'ang yin

傳經堂珍藏印

ch'uan-shen (to transmit the spirit) 傳神

Chuang Tan-an 莊澹菴

Chung-kuang 重光

Ho-yang (Kuo Hsi) 河陽

Ho Yüan-yü 何瑗玉

Hou Ch'uan 侯銓

Hsi-chin 錫晉

Hsi-hsiang-chi 西廂記

Hsi-lu hou-jen 西廬後人

Hsi-lu lao-jen (Wang Shih-min) 西廬老人

Hsi-shuang 西爽

Hsi-t'ing 西亭

Hsi-t'ing Ho-tao-jen 西亭鶴道人

Hsia-an (Yeh Kung-ch'o) 遐庵

Hsia-shan t'u 夏山圖

Hsiang Hung-tso 項鴻祚

Hsiang-pi (Wang Chien) 湘碧

Hsiang-ts'ao-an 香艸盦

Hsiang-ts'ao-an chu-jen 香艸盦主人

Hsiang Yüan-pien 項元汴

Hsiao-hsiang 瀟湘

Hsiao Sung 小松

hsieh-i (to write ideas) 寫意

hsieh-sheng (painting from life) 寫生

Hsien-ch'ih (Yao Shou) 仙癡

Hsin-an 新安

Hsin-ch'ing chü-shih (Sun Yüan-hsiang)
心青居士

Hsin-yüan chü-shih (Hsü Pang-ta)
心遠居士

hsing (excitement) 興

Hsing-fu-an kan-chiu t'u 興福庵感舊圖

hsing-ssu (physical likeness) 形似

Hsing yü yen hsia hui 興與煙霞會

Hsü Ch'ing-yu (Hsu Chih-chien) 許青嶼

Hsü-hsi 徐熙

Hsü Nai-p'u 徐乃普

Hsü Pang-ta 徐邦達

hsü-shih (void and solid) 虛實

Hsüan-ch'ing-shih 懸磬室

Hsüan-ch'ing-shih hua yin 懸磬室畫印

Hsüan-ho hua-p'u 宣和畫譜

Hsüan-ko 宣閣

Hsüan-tsai (Tung Ch'i-ch'ang) 玄宰

Hsüan-t'ung chien-shang 宣統鑑賞

Hsüan-t'ung yü-lan chih pao 宣統御覽之寶

Hsüeh chi t'u 雪霽圖

Hsüeh-p'u-t'ang yin 學圃堂印

Hsün-yang 潯陽

Hsün-yüan mo-ku 洵遠摹古

Hu-chün tu-hua 湖颿讀畫

Hu Hsiao-cho 胡小琢

Hu Hsiao-cho ts'ang 胡小琢藏

Hu-t'ien ch'un-se 湖天春色

Hua-ch'iao lao-p'u 華橋老圃

Hua-hsüeh hsin-yin 畫學心印

227

Hua Kuei (Hua Ch'uan)　華銈

Hua-shih　畫史

Hua-t'ing　華亭

Hua t'u liu yü jen k'an　畫畱留與人看

Hua-yüan　華源

Huai-yin Hu-shih chia ts'ang　淮陰胡氏家藏

Huai-yü-t'ing　懷雨亭

Huai-yün-lou　懷雲樓

Huai-yün-lou chien-shang shu-hua chih chi

　　懷雲樓鑑賞書畫之記

Huan-shan　環山

Huang Chün-pi　黃君璧

Huang-ho ch'iao-che　黃鶴樵者

Huang-ho shan-jen (Wang Meng)　黃鶴山人

Huang I　黃易

Huang Kung-wang　黃公望

Huang-liu-tzu　皇六子

Huang-shih Huai-hsüan-t'ang ts'ang

　　黃氏褱讓堂藏

Huang T'ing-chien　黃庭堅

Hui-tsung　徽宗

Hung-jen　弘仁

Hung-shou　洪綬

Hung-yu　紅友

I-chin　詒晉

I-chin-chai　詒晉齋

I-ch'ing (Pao Chün)　逸卿

I-chou chen-ts'ang　儀周珍藏

I-hsing　宜興

I hu mu-lan liang teng T'ai-tai tsai yu Huang-
　hai san su Wu-t'ai

　　一扈木蘭兩登泰岱再遊黃海
　　三宿五臺

I-kuan-hsien　一貫軒

i-p'in (untrammeled class)　逸品

I-shih (Yao Shou)　逸史

I-tzu-sun　宜子孫

I-yüan-hsien　意遠軒

Jan-hsiang-an　染香菴

Jun-chou　潤州

Jung-hsi chai t'u　容膝齋圖

Jung-t'ai pi-chi　容臺筆記

k'ai-shu (regular script)　楷書

K'an-hsi-chai　堪喜齋

K'an-hsi-chai shu hua yin　堪喜齋書畫印

Kang-chou Li-shih Jih-tung chen-ts'ang

　　岡州李氏日東珍賞

Kao Hsiang　高翔

Kao I-hung　高逸鴻

Kao K'o-kung　高克恭

kao-yüan (high distance)　高遠

Ken-an chü-shih (Ku Wen-pin)　艮菴居士

Keng-yen (Wang Hui)　耕煙

228

Keng-yen san-jen　耕煙散人

Keng-yen san-jen shih nien ch'i-shih-yu-chiu　耕煙散人時年七十有九

k'o-hua ("carved" painting)　刻畫

kou (hook)　鈎

Ku-hsiang-lou ts'ang-pao　古香楼藏寶

ku-i (the antique spirit)　古意

Ku Lin-shih　顧麟士

Ku-shan　穀山

Ku-shang Huang Chün-yüan Tzu-lin shih so-ts'ang ming-jen tzu-hua chih chang　沽上黃濬源子林氏所藏名人字畫之章

Ku-tai shu-hua kuo-mu hui-k'ao fu-mu　古代書畫過目彙攷附目

Ku Tzu-shan mi ch'ieh yin　顧子山秘篋印

Ku Wen-pin yin　顧文彬印

Ku-? Wang-shih　古？王氏

Ku-yü　古虞

K'uai-chi shu-wu　會稽書屋

Kuan Mien-chün　關冕鈞

Kuan T'ung　關仝

Kuan tz'u chen-chi shih chüeh wei-che shen k'o-hsiao yeh　觀此真跡始覺偽者甚可笑也

Kuan-wu ching-shang　冠五精賞

Kuang-chou-shih ti-i-tz'u chan-lan hui　廣州市第一次展覽會

Kuang-han-kung ch'ung-kuang　廣寒宮重光

Kuang-yung ssu-yin　廣鏞私印

K'uang-lu　匡廬

Kuei Tzu-mu　歸子慕

Kuei-yü-ch'ih-an　歸于遲盦

Kung-ch'in-wang　恭親王

Kung-fu　功父

kung-li (fine and ornate)　工麗

Kung-shou　公綬

Kung tse shou　恭則壽

K'ung Kuang-t'ao　孔廣陶

K'ung Kuang-yung　孔廣鏞

Kuo Hsi　郭熙

Kuo-yün-lou-chu　過雲樓主

Kurokawa　黑川

Lai-ch'ing-ko　來青閣

Lai-shan chen-shang　萊山真賞

Lai-su-lou　來蘇楼

Lai-yün-kuan　來雲館

Lan-hsiang-kuan-chu　蘭香館主

Lan-t'ing hsiu-hsi t'u　蘭亭修禊圖

Lan-t'ing hsü　蘭亭序

Lan Ying　藍瑛

Lan Ying chih yin　藍瑛之印

Lang-an so-ts'ang　朗庵所藏

Lang-yeh　琅邪

li (constant principles) 理

li (1/3 mile) 里

Li 歷

Li Ch'eng 李成

Li Kung-lin 李公麟

Li Shan-lan 李善蘭

Li Ssu-hsün 李思訓

Li-tai liu-ch'uan shu-hua tso-p'in pien-nien piao 歷代流傳書畫作品編年表

Li T'ai-po ch'üan-chi 李太白全集

Li Ti 李迪

Li Tso-hsien 李佐賢

Li Tsung-k'ung 李宗孔

Li Tzu-yün shen-ting chang 李子雲審定章

Li wu-pen-t'ang ts'ang shu-hua chih yin

李務本堂藏書畫之印

Li-yang Ti Hsüeh-keng tzu Man-nung i-tzu Chia-sheng

漂陽狄學耕字曼農一字稼生

Liang 梁

Liang-ch'i Ch'in Tsu-yung chien-shang chen-chi 梁谿秦祖永鑑賞真跡

Lien-chou (Wang Chien) 廉州

Lien-hsüeh chien-ting 鍊雪鑑定

Lien-sheng shen-ting 蓮生審定

lin-ch'in (apple trees) 林檎

Lin-ch'uan ch'ing-chi t'u 林泉清集畫

Lin-hsia yeh-jen 林下野人

lin-ku (following the ancients) 臨古

Lin Yu-kuang 林有光

Ling-nan 嶺南

Ling Shu-hua 凌叔華

Liu-ju (T'ang Yin) 六如

Liu-ju chü-shih 六如居士

Liu Yü 柳堉

Lo Chen-yü 羅振玉

Lo Chen-yü yin 羅振玉印

Lo-shih Liu-hu 羅氏六湖

Lo Shu-yen 羅叔言

Lo T'ien-ch'ih 羅天池

Lou-shui 婁水

Lou-tung 婁東

Lou-tung Pi Lung Chien-fei-shih ts'ang

婁東畢瀧澗飛氏藏

Lu Hung 盧鴻

Lu Hung-chien 陸鴻漸

Lu-t'ai (Wang Yüan-ch'i) 麓臺

Lu Yü 陸羽

Lung-mien shan-chuang 龍眼山莊

lung-mo (dragon vein) 龍脈

Lung-su chiao-min t'u 龍宿郊民畫

Ma Chi-tsu yin 馬積祚印

Ma Ho-chih 馬和之

Man-nung p'ing-sheng chen-shang

曼農平生真賞

230

Mao-ch'in-tien chien-ting chang 懋勤殿鑒定章

Mei-ching shu-wu 梅景書屋

Mei-hua-an-chu (Wu Chen) 梅花盒主

Mei-tao-jen (Wu Chen) 梅道人

Meng-chih-chai 夢雉齋

Meng Tsung-hsien 孟宗獻

Mi Fu 米芾

Mi yu-jen 米友仁

mo (vein) 脈

Mo Ch'an 墨禪

Mo-chieh 摩詰

Mo-chieh hou shen 摩詰後身

Mo-ching ts'ao-t'ang hsiao-hsia t'u 墨井草堂消夏圖

Mo-li 莫釐

Mo-nung 墨農

Mo Shih-lung 莫是龍

Mountain Hermitage on a Clearing Autumn Day, see *Shan-chuang ch'iu-chi t'u*

mu (1/6 acre) 畝

Mustard Seed Garden Painting Manual, see *Chieh-tzu-yüan hua-chuan*

Naito Konan 内藤湖南

Nan-chou (Szechwan) 南州

Nan-hai (Canton) 南海

Nan-hai K'ung Kuang-t'ao shen-ting chin-shih-shu-hua yin 南海孔廣陶審定金石書畫印

Nan-hsün t'u 南巡圖

Nan-kung (Mi Fu) 南宮

Nan-pei-tung-hsi chih-yu-hsiang-sui wu-pieh-li 南北東西只有相隨無別離

Nan-t'ien (Yün Shou-p'ing) 南田

Nan-t'ien hsiao-yin 南田小印

Nei-fu t'u-shu 内府圖書

Ni Tsan 倪瓚

Ni-yen-lou 昵燕樓

Ni Yü (Ni Tsan) 倪迂

Ni Yün-lin hsien-sheng shih-chi 倪雲林先生詩集

Ou-po (Chao Meng-fu) 鷗波

pa-fen (formal script) 八分

Pai-men 白門

Pan-ch'an san-su 半禪三宿

P'an Chien-an 潘健盒

P'an I-chün 潘奕雋

P'an I-chün yin 潘奕雋印

P'an Shih-ch'eng 潘仕成

P'an Shih-ch'eng yin 潘仕成印

P'an Te-yü shen-ting 潘德畬審定

P'an Yen-ling yin 潘延齡印

Pang-shui chien-ts'ang 邦瑞鑑藏

231

P'ang Nai 龐耐

Pao-chi ch'ung-pien 寶笈重編

Pao-chih-lou 寶韡楼

Pao Chün 鮑俊

Pao Chün chih-yin 鮑俊之印

Pao Chün ssu-yin 鮑俊私印

Pao Hsi ch'ang-shou 寶熙長壽

Pao-ma-an 寶馬盦

Pao-sung-shih chien-ts'ang yin 寶宋室鑑藏印

Pao-wu-t'ang 寶武堂

Pao-yü-ko shu-hua lu 寶迂閣書畫錄

P'ao-chüan chü-shih 袍鋗居士

Pei-yüan (Tung Yüan) 北苑

P'ei-wen-chai shu-hua p'u 佩文齋書畫譜

P'en Chiang t'u 溢江圖

P'eng-ch'eng 彭城

Pi Chien-fei pi-chi yin 畢澗飛秘笈印

Pi Lung 畢瀧

P'i-ling 毘陵

p'i-ma-ts'un (hemp-fiber strokes) 披麻皴

p'i-p'a (guitar) 琵琶

P'i-p'a hsing 琵琶行

pien (metamorphosis) 變

Ping-heng ch'ang-shou 秉衡長壽

P'ing-sheng yu shu-hua p'i 平生有書畫癖

p'ing-yüan (level distance) 平遠

Po Chü-i 白居易

Po-kung so ts'ang 伯恭所藏

Po-shih (Li Kung-lin) 伯時

Po-yüan shen-ting 伯元審定

Pu erh fa 不二法

P'u-ting Yao Ta-jung tzu Li-huan hao Chih-feng chin-shih-shu-hua 普定姚大榮
字儷桓號芷灃金石書畫

rain-drop ts'un, see yü tien ts'un

Red Friend, see *Hung-yu*

Saitō Etsuzō 齋藤悅藏

San-ch'iu-ko shu-hua lu 三秋閣書畫錄

San-hsi-t'ang 三希堂

San-hsi-t'ang ching-chien hsi 三希堂精鑒璽

Sang-tzu-li 桑梓里

Seeking the Tao in Autumn Mountains, see *Ch'iu-shan wen-tao t'u*

Shaded Dwelling Among Streams and Mountains, see *Ch'i-shan yüeh-kuan*

Shan-chuang ch'iu-chi t'u 山莊秋霽圖

Shan-k'ou pu-yü 山口捕魚

Shan-pen-shih Hsiang-hsüeh shu-wu pin-ch'en-hou chih yin

山本氏香雪書屋丙辰後之印

Shan-shui ch'ing-hui (Wang Hui)

山水清暉

Shang-ch'iu 商邱

Shang-ch'iu Ch'en Ch'ung-pen k'ao ts'ang yin 商邱陳崇本攷藏印

232

Shang-hsia ch'ien-nien　上下千年
Shang-hsia ku-chin　上下古今
Shang-shu (Kao K'o-kung)　尚書
Shao Kuan　邵貫
Shao Lo-yang　邵洛羊
Shao Sung-lao　邵松老
Shen-an p'ing-sheng chen-shang

　　沈盦平生真賞

shen-ch'i (spirit and breath)　神氣
Shen Ch'i-nan　沈啟南
Shen Chou　沈周
Shen-hsien-chüan-shu　神仙春屬
shen-p'in (divine class)　神品
Shen Ping-ch'eng　沈秉成
Shen-shih Ch'i-nan　沈啟南氏
shen-ts'ai (divine color)　神彩
Shen Yeh-yün　沈野雲
shen-yuan (deep distance)　深遠
Sheng Yü shang-jen　聖于上人
shih (force, momentum)　勢
Shih-ch'i-sheng (Pao Chün)　石溪生
Shih-ch'ü pao-chi　石渠寶笈
Shih-ch'ü ting-chien　石渠定鑑
Shih-hao yü su ch'u suan hsien

　　嗜好與俗殊酸鹹

Shih-ku (Wang Hui)　石谷

Shih-ku-tzu　石谷子
Shih-lao (Wang Hui)　石老
Shih-ni ts'eng-shang　石尼曾賞
Shih-piao (Chia Shih-piao)　士標
shih-shan (rocky mountain)　石山
Shih-shih tao-jen　石師道人
Shih-t'ang chen-wan　碩堂珍玩
Shih-t'ien (Shen Chou)　石田
shih-yü　侍御
Shina Nanga Taisei　支那南畫大集
Shou-p'ing (Yün Shou-p'ing)　壽平
Shu (Szechwan)　蜀
Shu-hua chien-ying　書畫鑑影
Shu-ju (Chao Shih-kang)　叔儒
Shu-ming (Wang Meng)　叔明
Shu-pao (Ch'ien Ku)　叔寶
Shu-p'ing hua-chien (Weng T'ung-ho)

　　叔平畫鑑

Shu-tzu (Yün Shou-p'ing)　卡子
Shu Yün　書雲
Shuang-lin shu-wu　雙林書屋
Shui-hu chuan　水滸傳
Soochow　蘇州
Ssu-ma Hsiang-ju　司馬相如
Ssu-nung (Wang Yüan-ch'i)　司農
Ssu-pu pei-yao　四部備要

Ssu-weng (Tung Ch'i-ch'ang)　思翁

Su Shih　蘇軾

Su Shun-ching　蘇舜欽

Sun Pang-shui　孫邦瑞

Sun Yü-wen　孫毓汶

Sun Yüan-hsiang　孫原湘

Sung-chiang Li-shih Chung-chi chen-ts'ang
yin　松江李氏中及珍藏印

ta-ch'eng (great synthesis)　大成

Ta-ch'ien chü-shih　大千居士

Ta-ch'ien hsi　大千鉥

Ta-ch'ih (Huang Kung-wang)　大癡

Ta-ch'ih Fu-ch'un shan t'u i-chio jen-chia

　　大癡富春山圖一角人家

Ta Chin-shan　笪近山

Ta Chin-shan chia ts'ang yin　笪近山家藏記

Ta Chung-kuang　笪重光

Ta Chung-kuang yin　笪重光印

Ta-feng-t'ang chen-ts'ang yin　大風堂珍藏印

Ta-ming Ch'eng-shih Wei-an shang chien
t'u-shu　大名成氏畏庵賞鑒圖書

tai-chao (painter-in-waiting)　待詔

Tai Chin　戴進

T'ai-hang shan-se t'u　太行山色圖

T'ai-hu　太湖

t'ai-shih　太史

T'ai-ts'ang　太倉

T'ai-yüan　太原

Tan-shih　澹士

T'ang Tzu-wei　唐子畏

T'ang Yin　唐寅

T'ang Yün　唐雲

tao　道

Tao-chi　道濟

Tao-ning (Shen Yeh-yün)　道寧

T'ao Ch'ien　陶潛

T'ao-hua-wu　桃花塢

T'ao Keng　陶賡

T'ao Keng chih yin　陶賡之印

T'ao p'u sung chü　陶圃松菊

Te-che pao-chih shu-ch'uan chiu-yüan

　　得者寶之庶傳久遠

Te-yü hsin-shang　德畬心賞

T'eng-hua shu-wu t'u　藤花書屋圖

t'i (substance)　體

T'iao-hua-chai　苕華齋

T'ieh-yen-lu chen-ts'ang　鰈硯廬珍藏

T'ien-chen lan-man shih wu shih

　　天真爛漫是吾師

T'ien-ch'i shu-wu　田谿書屋

t'ien-hsia ti-i　天下第一

T'ien-sheng Nai-p'u　滇生乃晋

T'ien-sheng so-ts'ang　滇生所藏

T'ien shu-fu　田叔父

Ting-fu hsin-shang 定父心賞

T'ing-yün 停雲

Tōan-zō Shōgafu 董盦所藏書畫譜

Tora (Naito Konan) 虎

Tou-ho mi-lin 陡壑密林

tsa-pi (rubbed brush) 擦筆

Tsai-weng (Ta Chung-kuang) 在翁

Ts'ai Yung 蔡邕

Ts'ang-lang 滄浪

Ts'ao Chih-po 曹知白

Ts'ao-i (Yün Shou-p'ing) 草衣

ts'ao-shu (draft script) 草書

Tse-ku-hsi-chai 則古昔齋

Ts'eng ts'ang P'an Chien-an ch'u

曾藏潘健盦處

Ts'eng ts'ang Wang Chi-ch'ien ch'u

曾藏王季遷處

ts'un (brushstrokes) 皴

Tsung-po (Tung Ch'i-ch'ang) 宗伯

Tsung-po hsüeh-shih 宗伯學士

t'u-shan (earthen mountain) 土山

Tuan-ch'i Ho-shih Ch'u-an so-ts'ang i-shih
    wu-liang 端溪何氏遽盦所藏一時無兩

Tung Ch'i-ch'ang 董其昌

Tung Hsüan-tsai 董玄宰

Tung-t'ing yü-yin t'u 洞庭漁隱圖

Tung Yüan 董源

Tzu-ang (Chao Meng-fu) 子昂

Tzu-ching chih yin 子京之印

Tzu-chiu (Huang Kung-wang) 子久

Tzu-ch'un 梓村

Tzu-ho 子鶴

Tzu-ho (Yao Shou) 子和

Tzu-i-yüeh 自怡悅

Tzu-i-yüeh-chai shu-hua lu 自怡悅齋書畫錄

Tzu-mei (Su Shun-ching) 子美

Tzu-shan 子山

Tzu-shen (Wu Tzu-shen) 子深

Tzu Shih-ku 字石谷

Tzu-tzu-sun-sun yung-pao-yung

    子子孫孫永寶用

Tzu-wei (T'ang Yin) 子畏

Tz'u-ch'ien chen-shang 次乾真賞

Tz'u Yüeh-chih-yüan-t'ing shu-wu chien-
    ts'ang chen-chi

    賜嶽峙淵亭書屋鑒藏真跡

Wang Chi-ch'ien 王季遷

Wang Chi-ch'ien hai-wai so-chien ming-chi

    王季遷海外所見名跡

Wang Chien 王鑑

Wang Chien chih yin 王鑑之印

Wang-ch'uan 輞川

Wang Ch'uan t'u 輞川圖

Wang Hsi-chih 王羲之

235

Wang Hsi-chüeh　王錫爵

Wang Hsien-ch'en　王獻臣

Wang Hsien-chih　王獻之

Wang Hui　王翬

Wang Hui chih yin　王翬之印

Wang Lu-chih yin　王祿之印

Wang Ku-hsiang　王穀祥

Wang Meng　王蒙

Wang Nan-p'in yin　王南屏印

Wang Po-yüan　王伯元

Wang Shen　王詵

Wang-shih chien-shang chih chang

王氏鑑賞之章

Wang Shih-hsin　王時新

Wang Shih-min　王時敏

Wang Shih-min yin　王時敏印

Wang Wei　王維

Wang Wen-po　王文伯

Wang Ya-ch'en　汪亞塵

Wang Yüan-ch'i　王原祁

Wang Yüan-ch'i yin　王原祁印

Wei-yang (Yangchow)　維揚

Wen　汶

Wen Cheng-ming　文徵明

Wen Cheng-ming yin　文徵明印

Wen Fong, see Fong, Wen

wen-jen-hua (scholar painting)　文人畫

Wen Lin　文林

Wen-po　文伯

Wen Po-jen　文伯仁

Weng Pin-sun yin　翁斌孫印

Weng T'ung-ho　翁同龢

Weng, Wango H. C.　翁萬戈

Wintry Forests on Lake Shores, see *Han-lin ch'ung-ting t'u*

Wisteria Studio, see *T'eng-hua shu-wu t'u*

Wo ssu ku-jen　我思古人

Wu　吳

Wu Chen　吳鎮

Wu Cheng chih yin　吳徵之印

Wu-ch'eng　烏程

Wu Ch'eng-te yin　吳承德印

Wu-chin (Kiangsu)　武進

Wu Ch'ing-tu　吳清度

Wu-ch'ü (Kiangsu)　吳趨

Wu-hsia (Szechuan)　巫峽

Wu Hu-chün　吳湖颿

Wu Hu-chün yin　吳湖颿印

Wu Hu-fan　吳湖帆

Wu Hua-yüan yin　吳華源印

Wu-i-chai ching-chien hsi　無逸齋精鑑璽

Wu Li　吳歷

Wu-men Wang Yüeh-hsien chen-ts'ang shu-hua p'u　吳門王月軒珍藏書畫譜

Wu-mu-shan-ch'iao　烏目山樵

Wu-mu-shan-hsia-jen (Wang Hui)　烏目山下人

Wu Pi-ch'eng chien-ting yin　吳璧城鑒定印

Wu Po-tzu chen-ts'ang　吳伯子珍藏

Wu-shih t'u-shu chi　吳氏圖書記

Wu-shih Yün-ch'ing-kuan so-ts'ang shu-hua　吳氏筠清館所藏書畫

(Wu?) Ssu-lan　（吳？）似蘭

Wu Tzu-shen　吳子深

Wu Wen-yin (hao Meng-ch'uang)　吳文英

Wu Wen-yü chuang (mounter)　吳文玉裝

Wu Yao-hsi　吳曜西

Wu Yüeh wang-sun　吳越王孫

Yamamoto Teijirō　山本悌二郎

Yang Chin　楊晉

Yang Hsiung　楊雄

Yang-lien　養廉

Yao Shou　姚綬

Yao Ta-jung　姚大榮

Yeh Hsin　葉欣

Yeh Jung-mu　葉榮木

yeh-kuang (pearl that glows in the night)　夜光

Yeh Kung-ch'o　葉恭綽

Yen-fou yüan-hsiu t'u　煙浮遠岫圖

Yen-ju hsin-shang　燕如心賞

Yen-k'o (Wang Shih-min)　煙客

Yen-k'o chen-shang　煙客真賞

Yen-ling (Kiangsu)　延陵

Yen t'an ch'un hsiao　嚴灘春曉

Yen Wen-kuei　燕文貴

Yen-weng (Wang Shih-min)　煙翁

Yin-lü-hsien shu-hua yin　蔭綠軒書畫印

Ying Ho　英和

Yonezawa Yoshiho　米澤嘉圃

Yu-ch'eng (Wang Wei)　右丞

Yu-chu-chü　友竹居

Yu-chu-chü chen-ts'ang shu-hua chih yin　友竹居珍藏書畫之印

Yu-chu shan-ch'uang　幽竹山窗

Yu-chün (Wang Hsi-chih)　右軍

Yu ho pu k'o　有何不可

Yu-shih　酉室

Yu-shih chen-ts'ang　友石珍藏

Yü-chai　玉齋

Yü-ch'ing shan-fang　玉磬山房

Yü-chuang man-pi　雨窗漫筆

Yü Fu　漁父

Yü-kang chü-shih　鬱岡居士

Yü-kang-sheng (Ta Chung-kuang)　鬱岡生

Yü-ku　愚谷

Yü-lan-t'ang　玉蘭堂

Yü-shan　虞山

Yü-shan Weng T'ung-ho yin　虞山翁同龢印

Yü-shan Wu Li　漁山吳歷

Yü Shih-nan　虞世南

Yü-shih so ts'ang　于氏所藏

Yü Shu Hua-t'u liu yü jen k'an

　　御書畫圖留與人看

yü-tien ts'un (rain-drop ts'un)　雨點皴

Yüan-chang (Mi Fu)　元章

Yüan-ch'ang (Chung Yu)　元常

yüan-ch'i (primal breath)　元氣

Yüan-ch'i Mao-ching　原祁茂京

Yüan-ch'ing　沅薾

Yüan-k'o (Yün Shou-p'ing)　園客

Yüan Yü-hsüan　阮玉鉉

Yüan Yü-hsüan ssu-yin　阮玉鉉私印

Yüeh-hsüeh-lou　嶽雪樓

Yüeh-hsüeh-lou shu-hua lu

　　嶽雪樓書畫錄

Yüeh-yang　岳陽

Yün-ch'ao hsin-shang　雲巢心賞

Yün-chen-ko t'u-shu chi　縕真閣圖書記

Yün Cheng-shu　惲正叔

Yün-hsi (Ts'ao Chih-po)　雲西

Yün-lin (Ni Tsan)　雲林

Yün-meng　雲夢

Yün Shou-p'ing　惲壽平

Yün Shou-p'ing yin　惲壽平印

Yün-tung (Yao Shou)　雲東

Yün-tung I-shih　雲東逸史

yung (application)　用

Yung Hsing　永瑆

Yung Jung　永瑢

? -ch'i yin-chang　? 器印章

? -hsien pi-chi chih yin　? 軒秘笈之印

238

Selected Bibliography

Bush, Susan, "Lung-mo, K'ai-ho, and Ch'i-fu: Some Implications of Wang Yüan-ch'i's Three Compositional Terms," *Oriental Art*, viii/3, Autumn 1962, pp. 120-127.

Cahill, James F., *Fantastics and Eccentrics in Chinese Painting*, Asia House Gallery, New York, 1967.

Contag, Victoria, *Die sechs berühmten Maler der Ch'ing Dynastie*, Leipzig, 1940.

Contag, Victoria, and Wang Chi-ch'üan, *Seals of Chinese Painters and Collectors of the Ming and Ch'ing Periods*, Hong Kong, 1966.

Edwards, Richard, *The Field of Stones: A Study of the Art of Shen Chou (1427-1509)*, Washington, 1962.

Fong, Wen, "The Orthodox Master," *Art News Annual*, XXXIII, 1967, pp. 33-39.

Fong, Wen, "Tung Ch'i-ch'ang and the Orthodox Theory of Painting," *National Palace Museum Quarterly*, vol. II, no. 3, January 1968, pp. 1-26.

Hu P'ei-heng, *Wang Shih-ku* in *Chung-kuo hua-chia ts'ung-shu*, Shanghai, 1958.

Huang Yung-ch'üan, *Ch'en Lao-lien pan-hua hsüan chi* ("Selection of Woodblock Illustrations by Ch'en Hung-shou"), Peking, 1957.

Kuo Mo-jo (ed.), *Chung-kuo pan-hua shih lüeh* ("Short History of Chinese Woodblock Illustrations"), Peking, 1962.

Lee, Sherman E., *A History of Far Eastern Art*, New York, 1964.

Shao, Lo-yang, *Wu Li* in *Chung-kuo hua-chia tsung-shu*, Shanghai, 1962.

Sirén, Osvald, *Chinese Painting: Leading Masters and Principles*, London, 1958.

Sullivan, Michael, "The Ch'ing Scholar-painters and their World," in *Loan Exhibition of the Ch'ing Dynasty*, The Arts Council of Great Britain, 1964.

Tung Ch'i-ch'ang, *Hua-yen* in *Hua-hsüeh hsin-yin* edition, iii.

Wang Hui, *Ch'ing-hui hua-pa* in *Hua-hsüeh hsin-yin* edition, iv.

Wang Shih-min, *Hsi-lu hua-pa* in *Hua-hsüeh hsin-yin* edition, iii.

Wang Yüan-ch'i, *Yü-ch'uang man-pi* in *Hua-hsüeh hsin-yin* edition, vii.

Wen Chao-t'ung, *Ch'ing-ch'u liu-ta-hua-chia* ("The Six Great Masters of the Early Ch'ing"), Hong Kong, 1960.

Wen Chao-t'ung, *Ming-tai ssu-ta-hua-chia* ("The Four Great Masters of the Ming Period"), Hong Kong, 1960.

Weng, Wango H. C., *Gardens in Chinese Art*, China House Gallery, New York, 1968.

Wu Li, *Mo-ching hua-pa* in *Hua-hsüeh hsin-yin* edition, iv.

Wu, Nelson, "Tung Ch'i-ch'ang 1555-1636: Apathy in Government and Fervor in Art," *Confucian Personalities*, edited by Arthur F. Wright and Denis Twitchett, Stanford University Press, 1962, pp. 260-293.

Yün Shou-p'ing, *Ou-hsiang-kuan hua-pa* in *Hua-hsüeh hsin-yin* edition, v and vi.